PHOTOGRAPHS

CONTENTS

TABLES

ILLUSTRATIONS

INTRODUCTION

The proper, adequate and satisfactory stowage and securing of items of cargo are of the utmost importance for the safety of the crew, the carrying vessel, and the items of cargo themselves. If items of cargo are not stowed and secured in a proper manner, bearing in mind the intended voyage and the time of year, those items of cargo might shift from their stowage position, and damage might be sustained by the item of cargo or the vessel, or ship's staff might suffer injury.

This guide will take the reader through some basic rules to be remembered on every occasion during the loading and securing of cargo, will describe where regulations, recommendations and general guidance can be found, will describe recommended methods to be used for particular items and types of cargo, and will then give some guidance upon the points to be remembered during passage-planning and the voyage itself. It is not intended that this guide will give details of precisely how to secure any particular items of cargo. It will set out the basics and point to publications which give the rules to be followed. This guide does contain information, such as for the calculation of lashings, taken from Codes, but only that which is essential for the clear understanding of the text.

Under the IMO Code of Safe Practice for Cargo Stowage and Securing, ships engaged in the carriage of all cargoes, other than solid and liquid bulk cargoes, are required to carry a Cargo Securing Manual. Such a manual gives, for the vessel for which it was prepared, guidance for the safe carriage of cargo items for which that vessel was designed and cargoes with which, therefore, the crew ought to be familiar. This guide has been designed for use alongside the vessel's own Cargo Securing Manual, and together with IMO and other publications.

Despite there being Codes of Safe Practice and publications giving advice on the safe stowage and securing of cargo, incidents continue to occur during which pieces of cargo shift and damage is sustained. It has always been recognised that, when ships' staff have greater knowledge and are more aware of hazards, those hazards can be avoided and accidents can be prevented. The object of this guide is to increase the seafarer's knowledge of the forces acting upon items of cargo, and of the basic requirement for the safe stowage and securing of cargo, and to help with the understanding of the Codes and Guidelines in order to aid loss prevention.

SECTION ONE - GENERAL INFORMATION

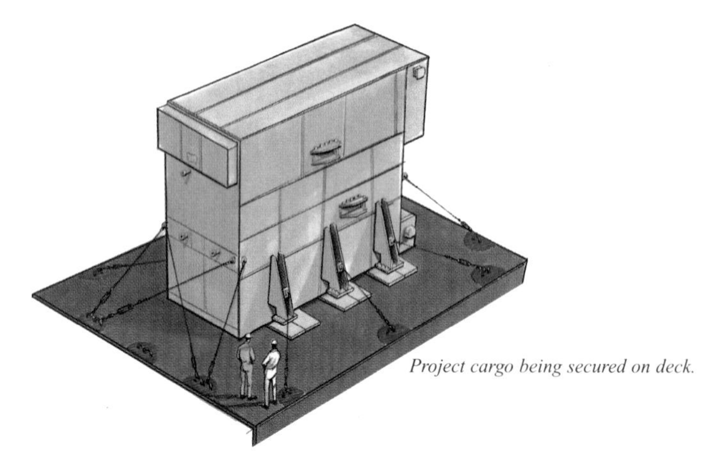

Project cargo being secured on deck.

BASIC RULES TO BE FOLLOWED

Here are some rules which are, essentially, common-sense and good seamanship practice. Whilst all pieces must be treated individually, it is not the case that some rules only apply to certain pieces of cargo and some to others - all of these rules should be borne in mind during every voyage and for every piece of cargo. The basic rules are as follows:-

- Be thoroughly familiar with the IMO Code of Safe Practice for Cargo Stowage and Securing and any subsequent amendments.

- Be thoroughly familiar with the contents of the vessel's own Cargo Securing Manual.

- Establish the weight of the item of cargo and, where possible, the position of its centre of gravity.

- Decide what types of lashing materials are to be used to secure the item, and then determine the maximum securing load (MSL) of the lashings.

- Examine the item of cargo and ensure that it is in a condition suitable for transportation on board on the current voyage and can be adequately and properly secured on board.

- The IMO Rule-of-Thumb method may be used to calculate the number of lashings required; that is, the total of the maximum securing load values of lashings on each side of a unit of cargo (port as well as starboard) should equal, or exceed, the weight of the item. The IMO Advanced Method may be used for heavy-lift items or where appropriate.

- The item must be stowed in a position where there is sufficient space for lashings to be led athwartships, forward, aft and downwards. There must be eye-pads or other strong anchorage points for the lashings to be attached to on all sides of the cargo item. Lashings should be independent one from another.

- Lashings should be attached to secure anchorages on the item of cargo, or should be taken around the item or around strong parts of the item of cargo. Lashings fitted to the cargo item should not be led in such a way that they damage either the anchorage point, themselves or the part of the cargo around which the lashing is led.

- Lashings should be balanced on each side and each end of the item of cargo, and therefore also in the athwartships and in the fore-and-aft line of the vessel.

- Ensure that all the cargo securing equipment is in good condition and is the most appropriate equipment for the job.

- Establish the maximum permissible loading for the hatch cover, deck or tank top onto which the cargo is to be stowed and ensure that the loading rate is not exceeded in way of the cargo. Where necessary and appropriate use suitable timber or other materials to spread the load over a greater area to avoid overloading.

- The item of cargo should be placed on firm and secure ground. An item of cargo should never be placed on, and/or secured to, something which itself is not secured to the vessel.

- Use dunnage materials, in the form of timber, plywood sheets, rubber mats, etc., to increase the coefficient of friction between the cargo and the surface upon which it is stowed. Avoid steel-to-steel contact. Ensure the surface is clean, dry, and free from oil and grease.

- Ensure that the stowage and securing of one item of cargo does not interfere with any other items of cargo and does not cause another item of cargo to be damaged.

- Examine, so far as is possible, cargo stowed within the item to be carried (that is, for example, on a flat rack container or in a road vehicle) to ensure that the cargo is properly stowed and secured on that unit or vehicle. If it is not, shippers or other on-shore personnel should be advised to rectify the problem before the containers or vehicle can be loaded.

- Ensure that the arrangement of the items of cargo and their lashings is such that routine inspections of the cargo and adjustment of the lashings can be carried out in all parts of the deck or compartment and that the stowage or lashings of particular items do not hinder or restrict those inspections which must be carried out throughout the voyage.

WHERE THE REGULATIONS, RECOMMENDATIONS AND GUIDANCE CAN BE FOUND

The IMO publishes SOLAS, Codes of Safe Practice, and Guidelines which set out requirements which must be followed and complied with. Additionally, there are a number of books which give recommendations and guidance for the stowage and securing of particular items of cargo.

INTERNATIONAL REGULATIONS

SOLAS

SOLAS stands for Safety of Life at Sea and the term comes from the International Convention for the Safety of Life at Sea which is convened by the International Maritime Organisation (IMO), at intervals, to discuss and adopt requirements and amendments thereto. The current publication, SOLAS Consolidated Edition 2001 is the consolidated text of the 1974 SOLAS Convention, the 1998 SOLAS Protocol, and a number of subsequent amendments.

SOLAS incorporates requirements with regard to all aspects of the operation of a vessel and, as chapter VI, Carriage of Cargoes. The chapter is in three parts, and Part A applies to the carriage of cargoes which, owing to their particular hazards to ships and persons on board, may require special precautions. Regulation 5, in Part A, deals with stowage and securing and in order to avoid any ambiguity that regulation is quoted in Appendix A of this booklet. Parts B and C deal with bulk cargoes and grain.

It must be remembered that SOLAS is being reviewed constantly and amendments are published.

Code of Safe Practice for Cargo Stowage and Securing

The CSS Code, as it is known, includes general principles for the safe stowage and securing of cargoes, definitions of terms in general use, some basic recommendations to be followed and some guidance with regard to actions in heavy weather and when cargo has shifted. Annexes 1 to 12 give guidance upon the stowage and securing of particular types of cargoes and appendices 1 to 5 quote other resolutions and circulars to be considered.

In 1994/1995 three amendments to the original text of the CSS Code and a new Annex 13 were published. Annex 13 gives the methods to assess the efficiency of securing arrangements for non-standardised cargo. This Annex gives a definition for the maximum securing load (MSL) and the method for calculating the MSL for lashing materials.The Annex also describes the Rule-of-Thumb method which is the basic method for calculating the required strength of lashings. Paragraph 7 gives the Advanced Calculation Method which may be used to calculate the external forces acting upon a single item of cargo and then whether or not the chosen lashing materials and number of lashings to be fitted are sufficient. Further amendments to the CSS Code were approved by the IMO in 2002 and a consolidated edition of the Code published in 2003.

The CSS Code is the document upon which Cargo Securing Manuals are based. It must be remembered that the Code is updated from time to time and further amendments will be published. Later in this guide a couple of the latest amendments will be mentioned.

Guidelines for the Preparation of the Cargo Securing Manual

The guidelines describe what a Cargo Securing Manual should contain and how that information should be laid out. The guidelines give definitions of terms and some useful information about certain cargo types.

Code of Safe Practice for Ships Carrying Timber Deck Cargoes
Timber deck cargoes are different from all other types of cargo carried on deck and are secured in a manner different to that which applies to all other cargoes. This being the case, a separate Code was devised a long time ago, the 1991 Code being the current version.

Code on Intact Stability
This Code contains the requirements for intact stability criteria for different types of vessel. The Code also gives details of information required on board, general precautions against capsizing and operational procedures related to weather conditions.

Safe Stowage and Securing of Cargo Units and Other Entities in Ships other than Cellular Container Ships
This resolution, attached as Appendix 1 to the CSS Code, gives some general guidance.

Elements to be Taken into Account when Considering the Safe Stowage and Securing of Cargo Units and Ships
This resolution attached as Appendix 3 to the CSS Code gives elements to be taken into account by the various parties involved with the stowage and securing of cargo units and vehicles.

Guidelines for Securing Arrangements for the Transport of Road Vehicles on Ro-Ro Ships
This resolution is attached as Appendix 4 to the CSS Code and gives detailed guidelines for securing arrangements for the transport of road vehicles on ro-ro ships including requirements for securing points on the ships' decks and on road vehicles to be carried.

NATIONAL REGULATIONS

All maritime nations issue their own regulations which are in addition to those which bring into force the international regulations. In the United Kingdom, Merchant Shipping Notices (MSNs), Marine Guidance Notices (MGNs) and Marine Information Notices (MINs) are issued. MSNs directly relate to the Regulations and the Codes and should be read together with those Regulations and Codes. MGNs and MINs contain additional guidance and information on particular subjects. In addition, there are the old M notices, which preceded the latest notices, many of which are still in force.

Agencies in the United Kingdom and in other countries produce instructions and guidance booklets which give recommendations with regard to the stowage and carriage of cargoes loaded at their ports.

INTERNATIONAL STANDARDS

ISOs are published by the International Organisation for Standardisation which is a worldwide federation of national standard-setting bodies.

Standards are issued on a wide range of subjects including the construction of ISO containers, the packing, handling and securing of freight containers, the construction and use of pallets and the construction and use of other types of packaging.

PUBLICATIONS

Thomas' Stowage
Thomas' Stowage (first published as Stowage The Properties and Stowage of Cargoes in 1928, the most recent edition having been produced in 2002) is, rightly, used throughout the

shipping industry for guidance and information about the properties and stowage of cargoes. The book gives a great deal of information about the stowage and care required for particular types of cargo.

Lashing and Securing of Deck Cargoes

First published as a book in 1994, gives in great detail how deck cargoes should be lashed and secured; many of the techniques described can, of course, also be used on under-deck stowed items.

Steel Carriage by Sea

This book describes all aspects of steel products from manufacture, through storage and on to carriage in ocean vessels. The book describes how steel items should be stowed and secured on board.

NOTE: details of all publications mentioned above can be found in the bibliography.

CARGO SECURING MANUAL

The booklet Guidelines for the Preparation of the Cargo Securing Manual was published by the IMO in 1997 to show how a manual should be arranged and what it should contain.

The purpose of a Cargo Securing Manual is to set out the standards for cargo securing devices used on board bearing in mind the type of cargo, the characteristics of the vessel and sea conditions which she might encounter. The manual should be easy to use and must contain information and guidance applicable to the vessel for which the manual was drawn up; the idea being that all of the information in the vessel's manual should be of use to those on board and information which relates to cargoes which are not carried should not be included in the manual. For example, details of cell guides and the carriage of containers need not be included within the manual for a logger and details of the carriage of logs need not be included in the manual designed for a cellular container vessel. The information given in the manual should follow the layout described in the Guidelines, using the headings and sub-headings in the order shown, and should contain the necessary information specific to the vessel. All manuals will therefore be in the same format, so that seafarers will become used to that format and will be able to use the manual on any vessel efficiently. After the manual has been prepared by, or on behalf of, the ship operator, it must be approved by the administration of the Flag State.

The Guidelines set out the format which must be followed in the preparation of all manuals. The manual will be divided into 4 chapters and appendices:

Chapter 1 - General

At the beginning of chapter 1 there should be a preamble which should include paragraph numbers 1, 2 and 4 of the preamble given on page 1 of the Guidelines booklet and the statement that the manual has been prepared in accordance with the guidelines. The preamble is given in Appendix B of this booklet. Chapter 1 will then go on to give definitions and general information relating to the vessel.

Chapter 2 - Securing devices and arrangements

Chapter 2 contains, in as much detail as possible, descriptions of the securing devices used on board the vessel, including the number carried, their strength in terms of breaking load and their maximum securing load (MSL). Tables listing the devices and sketches of individual pieces might also be included. Next should come some advice, and guidelines with regard to the inspection and maintenance of both fixed and portable securing devices. Periods between inspections should be given and how maintenance work should be carried out, there should also be a record of inspections and maintenance in an appendix attached at the back of the manual which should be kept updated. It must be remembered that pieces of lashing equipment must be kept in good working order without defects that might detract from their strength.

Chapter 3 - Stowage and securing of non-standardised and semi-standardised cargo

Chapter 3 includes information on the proper handling of securing devices and safety instructions about handling those devices. The chapter should then go on to give a section on the evaluation of forces acting on cargo units. This section should include tables or diagrams giving acceleration for the vessel in the transverse, vertical and longitudinal lines. The tables may be used for calculation of the forces as set out in paragraph 7 of Annex 13, Advanced Calculation Method. A worked example is given to illustrate how to progress with the calculation and what the end result gives you. The next section will give guidance with regard to the stowage and securing of non-standardised cargo and this is usually a re-write of annexes given in the CSS Code.

Chapter 4 - Stowage and securing of containers and other standardised cargo.
Chapter 4 gives details of the stowage and securing requirements for standardised cargoes, essentially containers and other unitised cargoes. There will be guidance on the use of container securing devices and on where and how containers may be stowed and stacked. Stack weights and the arrangement of containers within a stack are of great importance and proper securing, appropriate to the stack of containers in the stowage position on board, is of great importance and must be born in mind. Tables of acceleration will also be included in this chapter.

Appendices
Lastly the manual should include appendices giving a safety check list for entry into enclosed spaces, a record of inspection and maintenance of securing equipment, and any appropriate drawings or sketches.

MOVEMENT OF A VESSEL IN A SEAWAY

When a vessel is at sea the wind, wind waves and swell waves cause her to move. The greater the strength of the wind and the greater the height of the sea and swell waves the more the vessel will move. There are six types of motion, three are rotational and three are linear. Roll, pitch and yaw are the three rotational motions and sway, surge and heave are the three linear movements.

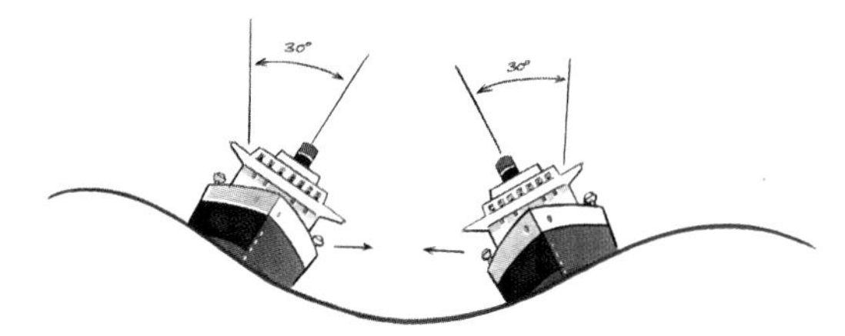

Rolling to 30° to port and to 30° to starboard, and swaying to port and to starboard, as each wave passes.

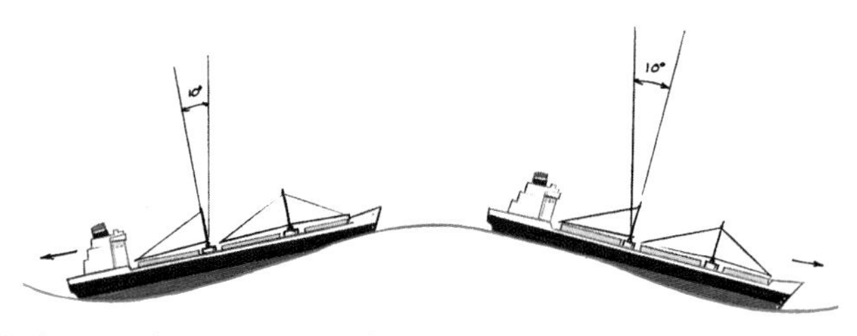

Pitching to 10° bow up and surging astern, and pitching to 10° bow down whilst surging ahead, as each wave passes.

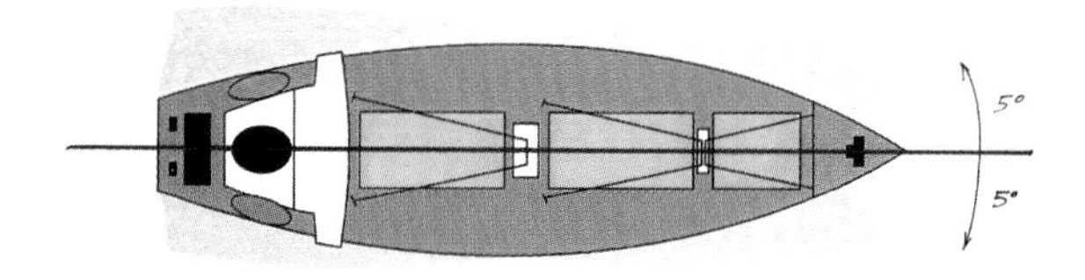

Yawing 5° port and 5° starboard as each wave passes.

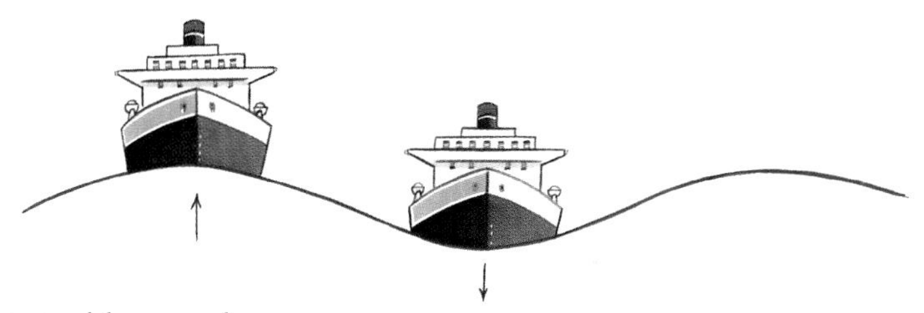

Heaving up and down as each wave passes.

Rolling, Swaying, Pitching, Surging, Yawing and Heaving - Ship Motions

The type, or types, of motion will depend upon the direction from where the wind and waves are approaching the vessel, relative to her course line. Clearly, if the wind and swell are from ahead the vessel will pitch and surge but will roll only a little, whereas, if she is experiencing a strong wind on the beam with associated high beam swell conditions she will roll and sway heavily but will not pitch very much. Normally, though, a vessel will experience all six motions at the same time, some to a greater extent and some to a lesser extent.

Generally speaking, the motions which are felt most by those on board, and therefore by the cargo being carried, are roll, pitch and heave. When considering the effect that a particular motion has on a piece of cargo it should be remembered that the three linear movements affect all parts of the vessel equally, irrespective of location, whereas the three rotational movements have a greater effect further from the vessel's centre of motion, which is normally close to the vessel's overall centre of gravity.

It is of course one of the responsibilities of the watch-keeping officer on the bridge to continuously monitor the actual sea conditions being experienced. Also, the officer must monitor the weather forecasts and other warnings in order to predict what weather and sea conditions the vessel is likely to encounter, particularly within the next few hours, so that adjustments can be made to the course and speed of the vessel in the short term, and in order that the passage plan can be adjusted to avoid sea areas of adverse weather or high swell conditions, in the longer term, so as to keep the vessel's motions to a minimum at all times. Keeping the vessel's motions to a minimum prevents the likelihood of accidents on board and minimises the possibility of items of cargo shifting.

THE VESSEL AND HER MOVEMENT - EFFECTS ON CARGO

The motions of a vessel in a seaway combine and produce three forces which act upon everything on board the vessel. Those three forces are perpendicular to each other and are, of course, in the vertical, athwartships and fore-and-aft line.

The magnitude of the forces, or accelerations, will depend upon the dimensions of the vessel, (her length, beam, depth and draught), her GM (metacentric height) and the wind and sea conditions being experienced. The smaller are the vessel's dimensions - the higher will be the accelerations; the larger the GM - the higher the accelerations, and, of course, where sea conditions produce larger ship motions, so the accelerations will be proportionally larger.

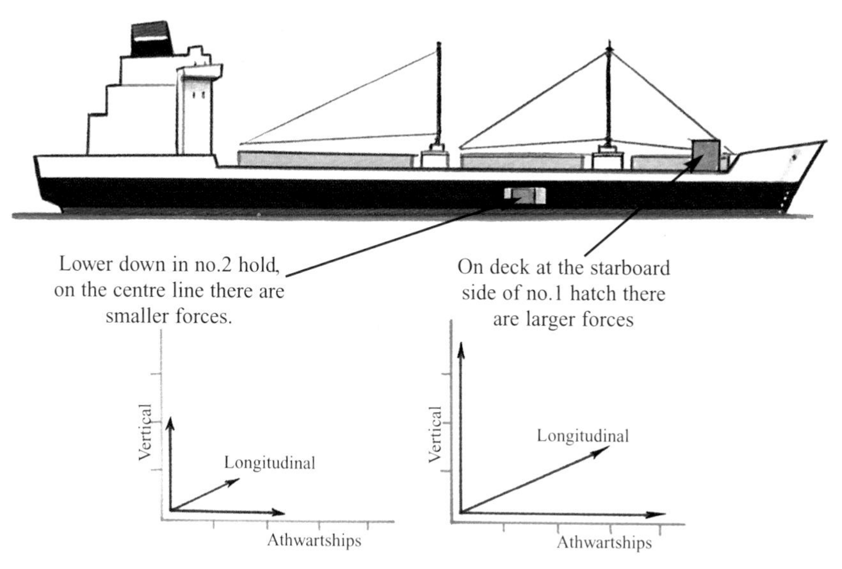

The combination of forces on board.

The acceleration forces act upon items of cargo and increase and decrease as the vessel rolls and/or pitches in one direction and then in the other. So, in fact, the accelerations are constantly changing from acceleration in one direction to acceleration in the other direction. These acceleration forces are transferred from the ship's structure through the lashings, the chockings and the dunnage under the item of cargo which causes friction between the cargo and the deck into the item of cargo. So long as the securings are of sufficient strength the item of cargo will not move relative to the vessel and the lashings, chockings and dunnaging will not fail. We now come to the question - "*Where are the acceleration forces greatest?*".

When the vessel rolls the ship's side plating moves through a greater distance, up and down, than does the hatch coaming, because the side plating is further outboard. When a vessel pitches the windlass on the forecastle moves up and down through a greater arc than does number one hatch. Thus, it can be concluded that the further the piece of cargo is from the vessel's centre of motion, in each of the three directions of motion, that is in the athwartships line, in the fore-and-aft line or in the vertical line, or in a combination of the three, the greater will be the acceleration forces acting on that item of cargo. Conversely, the acceleration forces are less the closer the item is to the vessel's centre of motion. Thus, if a piece of cargo which is sensitive to acceleration forces is to be carried on an ocean voyage it should be carried as close as possible to the vessel's centre of motion, which is likely to be fairly close to the vessel's centre of gravity.

Whenever considering the lashings and dunnaging of a piece of cargo its position on board, and therefore the likely distribution of acceleration forces which will be felt by that item of cargo during the forthcoming ocean voyage, should be born in mind. Following on from what has been said before, a piece of cargo stowed outboard to port or to starboard, or right forward or right aft, will need more lashings and dunnaging than will an item positioned inboard and amidships. The Advanced Calculation Method, in Annex 13 of the CSS Code, details of which should be in the vessel's Cargo Securing Manual, takes these factors into account when the formula is used to assess whether or not the chosen securing methods are sufficient.

As every seafarer knows, rolling causes more problems than any other motion. The vessel's natural rolling period is determined from her metacentric height and by her radius of gyration, these being determined by the structure of the vessel herself and the position of cargo and liquids on board. The radius of gyration is, in simple terms, the distance from the vessels centre-line out to the circle which represents the distribution of the rotational inertia of the vessel and her cargo about that centre-line. It is well known that winging-out the cargo will increase the roll period; this is because by loading cargo further to port and to starboard the radius of gyration is increased.

If the GM and radius of gyration are known the roll period of the vessel can be calculated by the use of a simple formula. However, although the GM is calculated during each voyage, the radius of gyration is not often accurately known. For this reason, and after much experimentation, a simplified formula to calculate the roll period using GM, or to determine the GM of the vessel using her roll period, was developed, as follows:-

$$T = \frac{C \times B}{\sqrt{GM}}$$

Where			
	T	=	Roll period in seconds.
	B	=	Vessel's beam in metres.
	C	=	Constant.
	GM	=	Metacentric height.

The constant is generally within the range 0.7 to 0.9, and 0.8 is often used when no other information is available. Smaller and finer-lined vessels will, generally speaking, have a constant closer to 0.7 whereas larger vessels and those with a larger block coefficient will have a constant closer to 0.9.

STABILITY

It is, of course, of great importance that the cargo should be stowed in such a way that upon completion the vessel has adequate stability for the intended voyage. The term 'stability' is used when describing the vessel's initial static stability and her dynamic stability which includes the calculation of information such as righting levels at certain angles. We will here only concern ourselves with the initial GM of the vessel because it is that figure which is used in calculations for basic roll period and in lashing calculations.

The term "initial GM" means the vessel's calculated metacentric height after the free surface effect has been applied.

MINIMUM GM

In order to ensure that the vessel has a satisfactory GM for the voyage, at both the time of departure from the load port and arrival at destination, the master often has to cope with the weights of deck cargo, under deck cargo, ballast and fuel when he is carrying out his pre-loading calculations. This is particularly so when a deck cargo of timber or containers is to be loaded and a maximum deadweight of that cargo is to be carried. It is often the case that some deck cargo must be shut out in order that sufficient ballast can be taken into double-bottom tanks to compensate for the top weight, in order to achieve a satisfactory GM.

The Code on Intact Stability gives, in chapter 3, the general intact stability criteria for all ships; that is to say, the requirements which must be met in terms of static and dynamic stability prior to the vessel's departure at the beginning of a passage. At section 3.1.2.4 it is required that:

The GM should be not less than 0.15m throughout the voyage.

That figure is, therefore, the minimum initial GM required for any vessel proceeding to sea. The only exception to this is in the case of a cargo ship carrying a timber deck cargo when the GM should not be less than 0.10 m in the departure condition, this being found in chapter 4 of the Code on Intact Stability, section 4.1.3.3.

MAXIMUM GM

With regard to the maximum GM, guidance is given for vessels carrying timber deck cargoes, but no other specific guidance is given in the regulations for any other situation. For timber ships, paragraph 2.5 of the Timber Deck Cargo Code states that the metacentric height should preferably not exceed 3% of the breadth in order to prevent excessive accelerations in rolling.

For a vessel having a beam of 25 m, a typical logger, the GM should not be more than 0.75 m. The requirements for the securing of a deck cargo of timber are based on a philosophy slightly different from that for other cargoes, as will be explained in the section dealing with timber cargo. For this reason it is essential that the GM of a timber ship is not excessive, such that, in turn, the accelerations associated with the rolling of the vessel are kept small.

The question then arises, for vessels not carrying timber on deck - *what is an acceptable range within which the GM of the vessel should be kept?*

Clearly, the size of the acceptable initial GM will depend on the size and type of the vessel. However, a guide for the upper limit is given in the Advanced Calculation Method in the CSS Code where a correction factor must be applied when the vessel's breadth divided by her GM is less than 13.

A guide for the upper limit is that the vessel's breadth divided by her GM ought to be less than 13.

The correction factor takes into account the fact that if a vessel has a large GM, and therefore the ratio of B/GM is smaller than 13, the rolling period will be short and the forces and acceleration generated will be large. For a vessel of a breadth of 30 m this means her GM should be less than 2.3 m, and for a vessel of breadth 20 m her GM should be less than 1.5 m in order to avoid the correction factor.

Using the roll period formula, given above, those breadths and GMs translate into roll periods of, for the larger vessel -15.8 seconds, and for the smaller vessel - 13.1 seconds. This is all in line with normal good seamanship practice where a short roll period should be avoided. Taking all of this into account it may be said that the GM of a smaller vessel should, ideally, be within the range of from about 0.5 m to 1.5 m and that the GM for a larger vessel should be within the range from about 0.5 m to 2.3 m. Masters of vessels should always seek guidance from the vessel's trim and stability book which will contain various examples of loaded conditions which give the GM, trim and other stability criteria, for which the vessel was designed.

LASHINGS, DUNNAGE, FRICTION AND SLIDE OR TIP OVER

When the appropriate stowage location for a particular item of cargo has been decided upon thought must then be given to dunnaging and securing the item so that it will not move. Items of cargo will either slide or tip over depending upon their shape and size, the position of the centre of gravity and the coefficient of friction between the cargo and the deck. There are many types of lashing equipment and many different types of dunnaging material, and only those which are appropriate for the particular cargo should be used, and used correctly, to reduce friction, to support the piece of cargo and to prevent it from moving. The different types of lashings and dunnage are described below.

LASHING MATERIALS

Wire Rope

Wire is a material very commonly used at sea, and the most common construction of wire used is 16 mm diameter, of 6 x 12 construction, with a fibre core. Such wire usually has a minimum breaking strength of about 7.7 tonnes. The size of the wire should always be appropriate to the size and weight of the cargo items being secured and it should also be borne in mind that for ease of use the wire should be flexible (wire of diameter 26 mm and of construction 6 x 37, for example, is not flexible enough for lashing purposes). Wire does stretch when in use; new wire will initially permanently stretch while it is settling and compacting, and will display an elastic stretch whilst in use, as load increases. The permanent constructional stretch is likely to be between about 0.25% and 1.0% of the length of rope, and the elastic stretch will be up to about 1.0% when the rope is under a load which is close to its nominal breaking load. Thus, when a new wire rope is used to lash a piece of cargo the lashing might stretch by as much as 2% of its original length when subjected to a high loading.

As is described later, in the section on maximum securing load (MSL), because wire will stretch and deform when subjected to high loadings in excess of 55% of the breaking strength, wire rope used for lashings is considered to be either single use when it is discarded at the end of just one voyage or re-usable when it is not discarded until it is visibly worn but is not exposed to high loadings which would cause weakening.

When wire is used to make lashings the wire must be formed into eyes or into loops by the use of wire rope grips. A rope grip comprises a U-bolt, two nuts and a cast steel saddle. There is only one correct manner in which an eye can be made in a wire using grips.

- The grips must be the correct size for the diameter of the wire in use;
- The correct number of grips must be used, see table below;
- All grips must be the same way round, with the saddle on the weight bearing part of the wire;
- The first grip must be close to the thimble if one is used;
- The other grips must be spaced six rope diameters apart;
- The cut end must be whipped or secured in some way and there must be no unlaying of the dead end of the wire and the dead end must be of length about six rope diameters;
- Lastly the nuts should be tightened until the U-bolt bites into the wire.

When an eye is made up correctly the wire will not slip through the grips until the load on the wire is about 70% of its nominal breaking strength.

Nominal diameter of wire rope in mm	Minimum number of wire rope grips
Up to and including 19	3
Over 19, up to and including 32	4
Over 32, up to and including 38	5
Over 38, up to and including 44	6
Over 44, up to and including 56	7

Table 1 - Minimum number of wire rope grips to be used.

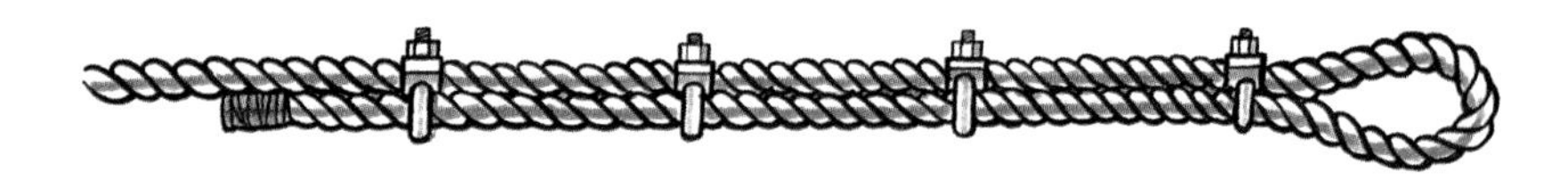

An eye in a wire rope properly made up using 4 grips.

Shackles and Turnbuckles

Shackles and turnbuckles are supplied in a number of types, shapes and sizes. These are used in conjunction with wire rope and chain lashings and the size appropriate to the size of the wire or chain, and appropriate to the lashing points on the piece of cargo and on deck, should be chosen. All threads should be well greased and free. The items should be in good condition, without defect or deformity.

Chains

Chains are, generally speaking, used for specific purposes only. Their main uses are for the securing of containers, items of ro-ro cargo, heavy lift items and timber deck cargoes. The chain will, in many cases, have been manufactured to the appropriate length and of the appropriate link size and type, and will have end fittings already in place, if appropriate. Chains can, of course, be used for the securing of other types of cargo but they are more difficult to use than are wire lashings and they do not render when led through or round items of cargo or lashing points. The main advantage of chain is that it does not stretch under normal loadings and can therefore be set tight when being fitted and will remain tight throughout the voyage, so long as the cargo does not move, compact or settle.

Fibre Rope

There are many different types of fibre rope, of both natural fibre and synthetic fibre, and most are produced in a wide range of diameters. Larger sizes are used for mooring purposes, variously on small craft and ocean vessels, with smaller sizes being used, amongst other things, for securing items of cargo. Fibre ropes have, however, characteristics which mean that they are not ideal for lashings. They stretch, both initially, when first tensioned, and during use. When wetted they will lengthen, and will shrink again when they dry out. They are weakened when knotted or spliced, and deteriorate when exposed to sunlight and sea water. Consequentially it is sometimes difficult to tension and keep a fibre rope tight. They should, therefore, be used to secure only lighter items, either alone or in conjunction with other materials, such as wire rope. Fibre rope can be used as frapping to tighten a wire rope, but a rigging screw should not be used to tension a fibre rope. Frapping being the use of a number of turns of fibre rope between, say, the eye in a wire rope and a D-ring to gain mechanical advantage to tighten the wire and to achieve strength in the number of turns. Fibre ropes have many uses but their limitation must be borne in mind.

Webbing

Webbing lashings are now widely used. They are easy to use, easily tightened and are manufactured in a range of different sizes and strengths. Webbing lashings are manufactured with a range of different end attachments and are provide with ratchet tensioners. Their most common use is for the securing of cargo onto road vehicles carried as ro-ro cargo, but they may also be used for the securing of a wide range of cargo items on board, many of which cannot be secured by other means, these include contact sensitive pipes and cylinders, yachts and other small craft, and cases or other items which are not provided with lashing points. Webbing has stretch characteristics similar to those of wire rope.

Steel Bands

Steel bands or straps are widely used for the securing of steel products in open stowage in the holds of vessels, and for the securing of many types of cargo items in closed containers or on flat rack containers, and on road trailers. Steel bands are lighter and easier to use than wire of the same strength and banding is much cheaper than is wire. For these reasons the securing of a stowage of coils can be completed in less time and at a lower cost when using steel bands rather than wire lashings, and riggers are likely to fit a greater number of steel band lashings than they would wire lashings. Thus, the stowage is better lashed. Similarly, steel bands are easier to use and more convenient for use with containers and trailers. The main disadvantage of steel band lashings is that they cannot be re-tightened, but they have the advantage that they do not stretch significantly and can be satisfactorily tightened so that the need to re-tighten them is eliminated. Steel bands must be fitted using the appropriate equipment, as recommended by the band manufacturer, that is by pneumatic tools (hand operated tools must never be used for the securing of cargo items) and that equipment must be operated at the correct compressed air pressure and the riggers using the equipment must be properly trained.

Sea Fastenings

The term sea fastenings is given to securing arrangements which comprise large section timber and/or steel girders which are variously bolted or welded together and to the ship's structure to form chocks variously against, under, over or around a piece of cargo to support that piece of cargo and to prevent it from moving. Sea fastenings are used for the securing of heavy items, those without sufficient lashing points and those which cannot be secured by any other method. Also, sea fastenings may be used in conjunction with conventional lashings of wires, chains or webbing straps.

Container Lashing Equipment

Container vessels are, of course, provided with specialised container lashing equipment. That equipment may comprise lashing rods or chains, turnbuckles, twist-locks, single and double cones, bridgefittings, deck studs and corner locators. Some vessels will be fitted with cell guides and others with tension-pressure elements for the securing of under-deck containers. There are also various other fittings, both fixed and portable, which can be supplied. Container lashing equipment is to be used only for the lashing of containers, and containers on container vessels must be secured using only the specially designed equipment.

CHOICE OF LASHING EQUIPMENT

It is of great importance that the lashing materials chosen for the securing of a particular item or shipment should be appropriate. For example, chains and wire ropes should not be used to secure rolls of tissue paper because the lashings will cut into the paper and cause damage when the cargo moves as the vessel rolls and pitches in the seaway. Similarly, webbing straps or steel bands are likely to be unsuitable for the securing of a 200 tonne piece of machinery simply on the basis of the number which would be required. Lashings appropriate to the size, weight and type of cargo must be used and those lashings must always be used in conjunction with appropriate pieces of dunnage material.

CARE OF LASHING MATERIALS

Lashing materials must be kept, when not in use, in a suitable clean, dry storage area away from chemicals or other stores items which might cause damage to the lashing materials. Moving parts of items such as shackles and turnbuckles should be kept lubricated and free. All pieces of lashing equipment should be thoroughly inspected at regular intervals and all damaged, heavily worn or otherwise defective pieces should be discarded or put to one side pending repairs. Whenever items are brought out of storage and into use to secure cargo, an examination should be carried out to confirm that they are still in satisfactory working order. When new pieces are brought on board they should be inspected to confirm that they are the items which were ordered and that they are in good condition. The Cargo Securing Manual should be updated as appropriate. Whenever the vessel's outfit of portable cargo securing devices changes, those changes should be recorded in the appropriate section of the Cargo Securing Manual. The appropriate record should be completed whenever routine visual examinations or periodic detailed examinations and re-testing of the devices are carried out.

DUNNAGE

The term dunnage includes the various materials which are used to protect, separate and support items of cargo.

Dunnage includes:-

- Timber in the form of flat boards, large section balks and the full range of sizes in between.
- Various types of paper including reinforced and water resistant.
- Polythene sheeting and other synthetic or natural fibre material sheeting.
- Air bags in a range of sizes.
- Various types of poles, woven mats, etc. made and used predominantly in the Indian sub-continent and the Far East.

Dunnage has many functions, but in connection with stowage and securing these are:-

- To protect cargo from contact with the vessel's steelwork, to avoid contact with water which might form as ship sweat or which might run down from above, for whatever reason.
- To support one shipment of cargo loaded on top of another, in the form of timber, plywood sheets or steel sheets and plates.
- To support cargo against tipping, in the form of timber shores or buttresses.

- To spread the load of the cargo across the hatch, deck or tank-top.

- To increase the friction between the base of the cargo item and the hatch, deck or tank top upon which it is stowed.

As with lashings, dunnage material which is part of the ship's outfit, and is not discarded at the end of a voyage, should be stored in a suitable clean and dry storage space, away from any chemicals or other items which might cause damage. At appropriate intervals the dunnage materials should be visually examined to determine whether or not any damage has been sustained, in which event, damaged pieces should be discarded. Whenever dunnage materials are brought into use, and when new dunnage is brought on board, the items should be thoroughly inspected for defects and for their suitability for the intended purpose.

FRICTION

Whenever two surfaces are in contact and are either static or sliding one over the other there will be a friction force acting against any force which is causing or is likely to cause movement. That friction force is dependent upon the coefficient of friction (μ) between the two surfaces. For a piece of cargo placed on the deck of a vessel the friction force, or rather the force required to overcome that friction force and therefore required to move that piece of cargo across the deck, can be calculated by multiplying the "weight" of the item (mass x gravitational pull) by the coefficient of friction of the two surfaces:-

$$F = \mu.m.g$$

Where:
F = Friction force.
μ = Friction coefficient.
m = Mass.
g = Acceleration due to gravity.

Thus, the larger the friction coefficient of the contact surfaces, the larger will be the force required to slide the item of cargo across the deck.

The magnitude of the coefficient of friction is dependent upon the nature of the two surfaces and whether or not they are lubricated. In paragraph 7.2.1 of Annex 13 of the CSS Code the most useful friction coefficients, so far as the securing of cargo are concerned, are given as follows:-

Materials in Contact	Friction Coefficient (μ)
Steel to Steel (wet)	0.0
Steel to Steel (dry)	0.1
Steel to Timber	0.3
Steel to Rubber	0.3
Timber to Timber (wet or dry)	0.4 *

* This coefficient of friction was introduced in the 2002 amendments to Annex 13 of the CSS Code.

Table 2 - Coefficients of Friction from the CSS Code.

Other useful coefficients drawn from a number of independent sources are given below. It must be remembered that results of experiments to determine the friction coefficient for two surfaces will vary between experiment and experiment.

Materials in Contact	Friction Coefficient (μ)	
	Dry	**Wet/Greasy**
Steel to Cast Iron	0.2	0.18
Steel to Timber	0.3 to 0.6	0.1 to 0.4
Timber to Timber	0.54 to 0.62	0.5
Timber to Rubber	0.8	0.7

Table 3 - Other Useful Coefficients of Friction.

The coefficient of friction between two surfaces is the tangent of the angle to which that contact surface must be raised in order that movement between the two surfaces will occur as a result of gravitational force alone, without any other external forces acting.

The coefficient of friction between timber and steel is 0.3. The friction coefficient is independent of the weight of the object pressing down on the surface and is also independent of the area of the contact surface. This means that a piece of timber dunnage, of any size or weight, lying on the deck of a vessel will move to the low side of the vessel when she is listed to about 17°; 0.3 being the tangent of 16.699°. Similarly, a heavy piece of machinery, of whatever weight, placed on ample timber dunnage on the deck of a vessel will also slide to the low slide when the vessel is heeled to 17°. That is, of course, with no lashings fitted.

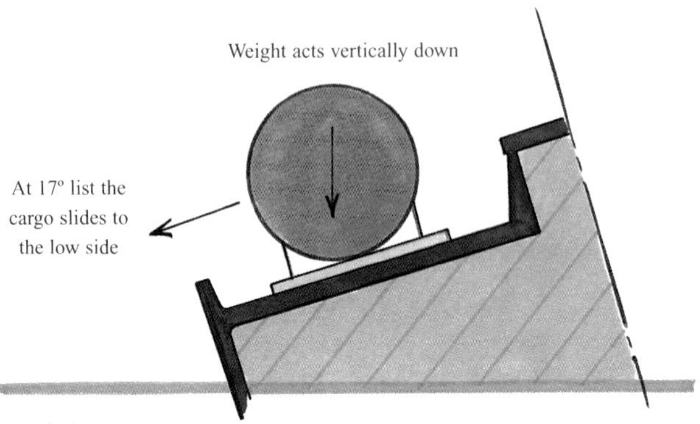

Cargo sliding on deck.

From the CSS Code table of coefficients it is clear that if there were no dunnage between the steel base of the piece of machinery and the steel deck the piece of machinery would slide at a much smaller list angle. If the steel deck is wet it is apparent from the table in the CSS Code that the piece of machinery would slide across the deck even with the vessel upright, the coefficient being 0.0. That figure has been given in the table more to represent the dynamic situation, with the vessel rolling and pitching, than a static situation. Of course the piece of machinery would not move simply because the deck is wet, but once the vessel starts to move the coefficient of friction may be considered to be zero and it is the dynamic situation against which we are trying to secure the cargo. Therefore it is also clear that when timber dunnage is fitted below pieces of cargo, but with no lashings fitted, they would slide across the deck at an angle greater than if there were no timber at all.

When a ship is in a seaway, and she is rolling and pitching, the angle of the deck to the horizontal will be changing throughout and therefore the relationships between the item of cargo and the deck upon which it is stowed are dynamic and external forces will be acting upon the cargo in all directions, as given above.

These additional external forces will cause a piece of cargo to slide over the deck at an angle less than that which is equivalent to the friction coefficient of the two surfaces. Lashings, when properly fitted and tensioned, will stop the piece of cargo from sliding across the deck. This is done by the components of the lashings acting variously vertically down and horizontally. Vertical components will effectively increase the friction coefficient which will mean that a larger external force will be necessary before movement takes place. Horizontal components will act in line with the external forces, again meaning that larger external forces will be needed before movement takes place.

The components of the lashings will also prevent a piece of cargo from tipping over.

SLIDE OR TIP

We then come to the question - *will it slide or will it tip over?*.

Items of cargo which have a low centre of gravity and a large base area are likely to slide before they tip over, whereas items of cargo with a small base area and a high centre of gravity are likely to tip over at a roll angle far less than that required for the piece of cargo to slide. This being the case, when deciding upon the type of lashings and dunnage to be used in the securing of the piece of cargo, its size, shape and the position of its centre of gravity must be taken into account. To prevent a piece of cargo from sliding, the coefficient of friction between its base and the deck must be increased as much as possible, e.g. by the fitting of rubber matting below the piece, if appropriate, and by fitting low-level chocking or lashings to act against the forces which will produce the sliding motion. To prevent the item with a high centre of gravity from tipping over, the item must be fitted with timber buttresses or shores, and/or lashings, fitted to the upper part of the cargo item. These, of course, being in addition to other chocking or lashing at lower levels which must be fitted to counter the always-present sliding forces.

RULE-OF-THUMB AND ADVANCED METHODS

Annex 13 of the CSS Code gives the two methods of accessing the efficiency of securing arrangements of non-standardised cargo, i.e. not container lashings. That is to say either of the two methods - the Rule-of-Thumb method or the Advanced Calculation Method - may be used to establish whether or not the chosen system of lashings is sufficient to prevent the piece of cargo moving during an ocean voyage, provided severely adverse weather conditions are not encountered and provided the vessel is navigated in a proper and seamanlike manner.

It should be noted that amendments to Annex 13 were approved by the IMO in 2002 and therefore references to the amended Annex 13 will be made here.

It should also be noted that the two methods are for the assessment of the efficiency of securing devices, that is lashing, and dunnage below the piece of cargo to increase friction, but no account is taken in the calculations of the anti-tipping or anti-sliding forces set up by the use of timber chocking or timber buttressing fitted against a piece of cargo, or any sea fastenings. Also, the calculation methods are for the assessment of arrangements fitted to a single item of cargo which is free standing upon the tank-top, deck or hatch covers.

A presentation of the methods described in Annex 13 will be given in the Cargo Securing Manual of a vessel, given in a form suited to that particular vessel and the equipment on board.

MAXIMUM SECURING LOAD

For the purposes of the calculations here concerned the "maximum securing load" (MSL) of any device is used rather than its breaking strength. The MSL is defined in the CSS Code as the load capacity for a device used to secure cargo. The MSL of a securing device is a proportion of its breaking strength, as is the safe working load of a cargo gear wire, but here the proportion depends upon the type of device. As it says in the CSS Code:

Maximum securing load is to securing devices as safe working load is to lifting tackle.

The MSL proportions for different devices are given in the following table:-

Material	MSL
Shackles, rings, deckeyes, turnbuckles of mild steel	50% of breaking strength
Fibre rope	33% of breaking strength
Web lashing	50% of breaking strength *
Wire rope (single use)	80% of breaking strength
Wire rope (re-useable)	30% of breaking strength
Steel band (single use)	70% of breaking strength
Chains	50% of breaking strength

* Web lashing figure amended from 70% to 50% by the 2002 amendments to Annex 13 of the CSS Code.

Table 4 - Determination of MSL from breaking strength.

The Code suggests that where a particular device has been assigned a "safe working load" then that "safe working load" should be substituted for the MSL, provided the "safe working load" is equal to or exceeds the MSL as calculated from its breaking strength. Similarly, some devices will be given a permissible working load, for example lashing chains provided on board a log carrying vessel, in which case the working loads should be used as the MSL of the device.

It should, of course, be remembered that any lashing is only as strong as the weakest link, and that the MSL value of the weakest part of any combined lashing must be used in any calculation. For example, if a wire is shackled to a strong point on a piece of cargo and attached via a turnbuckle and a shackle to a deck D-ring, the MSL of the weakest device, which might be one of the shackles or the D-ring, must be used in any calculations.

The MSL percentages were derived from consideration of a number of factors. First of all, they are based on the understanding that the devices are in satisfactory working and lubricated condition, and not in any way damaged, corroded or wasted. Any damaged, corroded and wasted securing devices should, as mentioned above, be set to one side for repair or should be discarded by the appropriate method, they should not be used for the securing of cargo. Experiments were conducted at testing establishments on a range of lashing devices, both fixed and portable, and a set of results was evolved. Those results were re-checked by experts in a number of maritime nations. Safety factors were then applied, as appropriate, to the findings obtained by the tests and experiments, and the final table of MSLs, given as percentages of breaking strength, was produced.

The explanation as to how the percentages were derived is as follows.

Mild Steel Shackles, Rings, etc. and Chains

A mild steel shackle, ring, etc. has a yield strength of about 60% of its breaking strength. That is to say, those items will start to deform at a loading which is equal to 60% of its breaking strength.

The MSL was therefore set at 50% of the breaking strength so that mild steel items, and chains which are made of high tensile steel, will not deform during usage and can therefore be used time and again.

Wire Rope - Single Use and Re-Usable

Wire rope has no specific yield limit but elongates steadily until it fails. Experiments with lashing wires have shown that in order to keep a wire in good condition and therefore to avoid any permanent elongation, it must not be exposed to peak loadings in excess of 55% of the breaking strength. Also, frequent loadings of more than 15% should be avoided. That is to say if a wire is not exposed to loadings of more than 55% and loadings of more than 15% are not frequent the wire will remain in good condition without any deformation of the wires. From these findings and following the application of safety factors it was decided that wires which were part of the ship's outfit, and therefore would be re-used time and again, should have an MSL of 30% of their breaking strength in order to avoid the possibility of damage to the wire, whereas for a wire which is brought on board for a single, one trip use and therefore would be discarded at the end of the voyage whether or not any deformation of the wire had been suffered, an MSL of 80% of the breaking strength was appropriate. With regard to the use of wire rope grips to form eyes in wire lashings, experiments have disclosed that wire will slip through the grips at a load of about 70% of its nominal breaking strength. Thus, it must be recommended here that when single use wire rope is being used in conjunction with rope grips the MSL should be considered to be 70% of the breaking strength.

Fibre Rope

Fibre rope is often knotted and tensioned by the use of the Spanish windlass method (tightening turns of rope by twisting them by means of a stick). Thus, when in use it will not retain its full breaking strength and one-third of that strength appeared to be a commonsense figure for the MSL.

Steel Bands

Steel bands are also a one way material. During use, slight permanent elongation of the bands might occur, permanently weakening the band but the bands will be discarded at the end of the voyage, in any event. Thus, MSL of 70% of the breaking strength of the steel band is reasonable.

Web Lashings

Web lashings are, mostly, re-usable. Webbing has stretch characteristics similar to wire rope but does not deform at high tension as wire rope does. The figure of 70% of breaking strength was originally used for the MSL but the 2002 amendments recommend 50% of the breaking strength, as noted in the table above.

RULE-OF-THUMB METHOD

This is a simple method which may be used for the assessment of lashings fitted to a piece of cargo anywhere on board the vessel. The method does not take into account the size of the vessel, her stability or loaded condition, or the season or area of operation.

The method assumes that the item of cargo is adequately dunnaged to provide friction against sliding and assumes that lashings are fitted at an angle no greater than 60° to the horizontal. Any lashings which are at angles greater than 60° to the horizontal should not be included in the number of lashings in the assessment calculation.

The Rule-of-Thumb is as follows:-

The total of the MSL values of the securing devices on each side of the unit of cargo (port as well as starboard) should be equal to the weight of the unit.

The authors of Annex 13 have chosen to calculate weights and strengths in kN where 1kN ≈ 100 kg. However, so long as everything is in the same units it doesn't really matter, when using the Rule-of-Thumb, which unit, tonnes or kN, is used, and indeed to work out everything in tonnes might be easier.

The process of assessing the efficiency of the securing arrangements by this method is therefore quite simple and straight forward. The total weight of the unit must be established and the total of the MSLs of the lashing devices on each side must equal that total weight. An amount of commonsense and good seamanship practice must be observed in order for the rule to work efficiently. Remember the basic rules:-

- There must be a balanced number of lashings on each side of the unit, that number depending upon the size, shape and weight of the unit.
- Some of the lashings should have a fore-and-aft component as well as an athwartship component.
- Lashings which are led directly forward or directly aft, and therefore have no athwarthship component, should not be included in the assessment calculations.

- Lashings which lead down from the unit at an angle of more than 60° to the horizontal should not be included in the assessment calculations. Such lashings prevent tipping but not sliding.

- All lashings should be made up in the same way, comprising the same components, so that they have the same elasticity.

Thus we have a calculation method which demonstrates that, when a vessel rolls heavily to port and to starboard, the item of cargo will be sufficiently secured such that it will not shift under normal circumstances.

The Rule-of-Thumb method is an assessment of the effectiveness of the athwartships components of the lashings. Whenever using this method the overall arrangement of the lashings should be borne in mind to ensure that there are sufficient fore-and-aft lashings as well as the required number leading athwartships.

A tried and tested formula is to have 40% of the lashings' strength to port and 40% to starboard, with 10% leading forward and 10% leading aft; the 40:40:10:10 rule.

ADVANCED METHOD

The Advanced Calculation Method, given in section 7 of Annex 13 of the CSS Code, is a more precise calculation which assesses the efficiency of securing arrangements in both the athwartships line and the fore-and-aft line. The method is a calculation in four parts. Those four steps progressively set out and determine basic information needed, the external forces acting on the cargo, the anti-sliding and anti-tipping components of the securing arrangements and, finally, whether or not the securing arrangements are sufficient to keep the cargo from shifting.

The four steps are:-

Step One
All the basic information about the vessel, the piece of cargo and its stowage location should be obtained and listed, and the primary calculations completed.

Step Two
The external forces which are likely to act upon the item of cargo are calculated.

Step Three
The effectiveness and strength of all the individual lashings in each of the four directions is calculated.

Step Four
An assessment is made to establish whether or not the effectiveness of the combination of the friction and lashings exceeds the likely external forces.

If the combinations of friction and the lashing strength exceed the external forces in both the athwartships line and the fore-and-aft line then those lashings are sufficient for the voyage, but if any of the combinations of friction and lashing strength is less than the external force in that direction then additional lashings must be added or the friction must, somehow, be increased.

In **Appendix C** is a detailed description of how the Advanced Calculation Method works and how it can be used in practice. In **Appendix D** there is worked example and a calculation sheet setting out the assessments and as **Appendix E** a blank version of the calculation sheet.

WHICH METHOD TO USE

The worked example and the calculation in **Appendix D** show that a boiler is satisfactorily lashed in all four directions because the six anti-movement forces, acting against sliding and tipping, are all greater than the external forces by an acceptable safety margin.

If the voyage in the example had been earlier in the year such that the vessel was crossing the Gulf of Arabia during the south-west monsoon season, or if adverse conditions were forecast for the North Atlantic, consideration would have to be given to increasing the number or strength of the lashings to take into account the probability that the adverse weather conditions would cause an increase in the basic acceleration data which would, in turn, increase the external forces acting upon the boiler. The rule is that the weather conditions likely to be encountered on the voyage must always be taken into account when determining the number and strength of the lashings.

The worked example in **Appendix D** shows that the boiler is satisfactorily lashed using six lashings on each side. The question arises - *would the same lashings satisfy the Rule-of-Thumb method?*

The Rule-of-Thumb is - the total of MSL values of the securing devices on each side of the unit of cargo should equal the weight of the unit.

Weight of boiler	=	81.7 tonnes.
Total MSL each side	=	81.7 tonnes or 817 kN.
Securing devices' MSL	=	9.24 tonnes or 92.4 kN.
6 devices each side	=	55.44 tonnes or 554.4 kN each side.
Conclusion	=	Insufficient lashings.
Requirement	=	9 devices of MSL 9.24 tonnes to give 83.16 tonnes or 831.6 kN each side.

This exercise shows that if it is possible to use the Advanced Method it is likely to mean that fewer securing devices are needed, but the calculation can only be used if all the information to complete the calculation is available, otherwise the Rule-of-Thumb must be used.

AMENDMENTS TO ANNEX 13 OF THE CSS CODE

The IMO approved amendments to Annex 13 of the CSS Code in 2002. A couple of those amendments have been mentioned above, for example the timber to timber friction coefficient of 0.4 and the revised MSL for web lashing at 50% of breaking strength rather than 70%. There are a few other amendments and re-arrangements of the paragraphs. Also, there is a new sub-section 7.3 which gives an alternative method for the estimation of the balance of forces and takes into account the angle between the lashing and the athwartships line of the vessel. A consolidated edition of the CSS Code was published in 2003.

CAUTION

The calculations have been formulated with a number of basic understandings in mind, most of which are good seamanship practice.

It is assumed that the vessel will not roll to an angle greater than 30° to port and to starboard and that she will not pitch heavily or slam into on-coming swell waves. Also, it is understood that the vessel will not be running before large stern or quartering seas such that excessive rolling and pitching motions are experienced. If the vessel's motions are very large then clearly the accelerations used within the calculations will be incorrect. The good seamanship answer to this is that when the vessel is approaching an area of adverse weather and/or high sea and swell conditions, actions should be taken to minimize the motion of the vessel by an alternation of course and/or speed. As it says in chapter 6 of the Timber Deck Cargo Code:

The lashings were not designed to provide a means of securing against imprudent ship handling in heavy weather. There can be no substitute for good seamanship.

The Advanced Calculation Method uses the "worst case approach", and therefore there ought to be ample reserve of strength to allow for unavoidable excessive motions of the vessel and errors in the estimation of the strengths of the lashing devices, the imbalance of the lashing devices and the angles and distances involved. However, it must be remembered that when measuring the securing angles and the lengths of levers the more accurate those measurements are the more accurate will be the results of the calculations.

The object of the Advanced Calculation Method is to establish whether or not the external forces are exceeded by the anti-sliding and anti-tipping forces. If it is found that there is no excess then clearly additional lashings need to be fitted. If in doubt, play is safe and fit more lashings.

The Advanced Calculation Method allows a reduced number of lashings to be used when compared with the Rule-of-Thumb method, see the comparison given in the worked example above. However, to take advantage of the reduced number of lashings the Advanced Calculation Method must be done correctly and completely. If all of the information is not available, for example the exact position of the centre of gravity of the item of cargo, the method cannot and must not be used. If there is any doubt whatsoever the Rule-of-Thumb, and all the guidance given in the sub-section above, must be used to assess the lashings applied to the item of cargo.

TANK-TOP STRENGTH CALCULATIONS

During the design stage of a new building the size of the various structures is decided upon. Those structures include deck and tank-top plating, under-deck stiffening members, double-bottom longitudinal and athwartships stiffening members, etc., and from the scantlings of those members the naval architects calculate the strength of the vessel's weather deck, 'tween decks if she has any, and the tank-top. Such a calculated strength is, of course, an absolute strength and cannot be used for cargo loading purposes. However, from those strength figures, and using safety factors (for example for corrosion) and other considerations, agreement will be reached between the naval architects of the shipbuilder and the naval architects of the Classification Society providing the necessary approvals, as to maximum permissible loadings, given in tonnes per metre squared (tonnes/m^2) for each deck and the tank-top, and also, usually the hatch covers. Those figures will remain in force throughout the lifetime of the vessel, so long as no structural changes are made.

The maximum permissible load figures are given on various ship's plans, for example the capacity plan, the midship section plan, and possibly also on-deck plans, and will also be quoted in the ship's trim and stability booklet and in the Cargo Securing Manual.

If the maximum permissible loading is exceeded in way of cargo items or blocks of cargo units, there is a strong possibility that the deck, 'tween deck or tank-top plating, and the under-deck stiffening members, will sustain damage when the vessel rolls or pitches in the seaway, if not before. Thus, it is essential to know the loading rate in way of heavy items of cargo and to ensure that the weight of cargo is spread out evenly over the deck, 'tween deck or tank-top plating to reduce the loading rate to below the maximum permissible loading rate. Similarly, it is essential to know the loading rate in way of blocks of cargo.

The maximum permissible weight of a cargo item or a block of cargo units is calculated as follows:-

Tonnage = Area of deck or tank-top (m^2) x maximum permissible loading (tonnes/m^2)

The formula can of course be used in reverse to establish the minimum area over which the weight of an item of cargo or block of cargo units must be spread.

Area of deck or tank-top (m^2) = Tonnage / maximum permissible loading (tonnes/m^2)

Deck and tank-top maximum permissible loadings range from around 1.5 tonne/m^2 for hatch covers, through to around 5 tonnes/m^2 for weather decks and 'tween decks, to within the range from around 10 tonnes/m^2 to perhaps 25 tonnes/m^2 for tank-tops. A bulk carrier designed for alternate loading of heavy bulk cargoes will have the strongest tank-top structures.

SECTION TWO - CARGO SPECIFIC INFORMATION

BREAK-BULK ITEMS

Loading break-bulk cargo.

Break-bulk cargo items include all classes of cargo which do not come under a specific heading, as do heavy-lift items and ro-ro cargo, and therefore do not have specific requirements in terms of stowage and securing. That does not mean, however, that there are no rules to be followed with regard to the safe carriage of such items. The CSS Code includes some guidance on the safe stowage and securing of portable tanks, portable receptacles and unit loads, in Annexes 2, 3 and 12 respectively, and that guidance can be applied to the carriage of most break-bulk, or general cargo items.

The items to be dealt with in this section (although there are many other types of commodity) include; cartons, pallets, cases, crates, rolls, reels, bales, tanks, vessels, unit loads.

The above listed items have two things in common; they have no lashing points, and they either cannot be loaded one atop another or they have a limited over-stow load. Many types of carton might be suitable for stacking nine high, but no more, whereas large reels of cable cannot be stowed one atop another.

The fundamental rule with break-bulk cargo is:

Establish the strengths and weaknesses of the items in terms of possible over-stowing capacity and susceptibility to damage from horizontally aligned forces, motions or contacts, and then decide upon the best manner in which the items are to be stowed and secured.

As is the case for all types of cargo there are a number of points to be remembered and basic rules to be followed when stowing and securing break-bulk items. These can be summarised as follows:

- The cargo compartment should be clean and dry so that the cargo items are not contaminated or wetted.

- The strength of the tank-top or deck area should be borne in mind when loading heavy items in order that the maximum permissible loading is not exceeded. Appropriate timber dunnage should be used where necessary to spread the load of the cargo items.

- Appropriate types and amounts of dunnage materials should be used to increase friction, and to protect, support and separate the items of cargo.

- The best method of securing the items of cargo should be decided upon; this might be direct lashings to the item or items, it might be lashings around the pieces of cargo, or maybe timber supports against blocks of cargo, or a combination of these.

- The way in which the cargo is stowed will depend upon the type of cargo. Some items should be stowed in blocks against a bulkhead and other types should not be stowed against each other or against bulkheads but should be stowed and secured individually.

- When stowing different types of cargo in blocks ensure that the items lower down in the stowage have sufficient strength to support the items higher up. Never stow heavy items over soft items of cargo.

- Items such as tanks or modules which have a long side and a short side should be stowed with their long side in the fore-and-aft direction.

- There should be a means of safe access into the cargo compartment or along the deck so that inspections of the cargo and their securing arrangements can be carried out safely by ship's staff during the ocean voyage.

Guidance with regard to different types of break-bulk cargo is set out below.

CARTONS, PALLETS, DRUMS, ETC.

Small and medium sized regular items such as cartons, pallets, drums, etc. can be block stowed together against a bulkhead or against the ship's side, or both, and then secured to that bulkhead and/or ship's side structure. When shipments of cargo are stowed in blocks the following points should be remembered.

- The deck or tank-top should be flat and flush, but if it is not timber or other dunnage materials should be used to level the surface so that the stowage block is itself level overall.

- Individual units should be stowed hard up against each other and hard up against the bulkhead and/or ship's side structures.

- Timber and/or paper dunnage should be used as appropriate in way of bulkheads and ship's side structures.

- The block should be stowed such that there are no void spaces between the cargo items. If spaces exist these should be filled with dunnage, which might include timber, air bags or whatever is appropriate.

- At each appropriate tier, of perhaps cartons or pallets, timber or plywood sheets should be used to spread the load of the upper tier cargo over the top of the lower tier of units and to ensure that the top of the lower tier is a flat and level surface onto which the next tier can be safely stowed.

- The lower tier units should not be "overloaded" by the weight of upper tier units.

- The block should be secured by a combination of dunnage and lashings. Dunnage, perhaps gratings or plywood sheets, should be positioned vertically against the block faces and then lashings, of wire, webbing straps, or whatever, should be lead around the dunnage at all levels of the stowage and then set tight to hold the dunnage in place and to minimise the possibility of movement of the block. Additional lashings to brace the primary lashings back to the bulkhead or the ship's side structure should be used as appropriate. The lashings should not pass directly over the cargo items because chafing damage might occur if direct contact is made.

REELS OF CABLE

Reels of cable come in a range of sizes and are dealt with here in isolation because they have special needs. Most are of timber construction although a small proportion of the larger size reels are of steel construction. The reels on which the cable is wound are, for the most part, for single trip use and will therefore be discarded when the cable is taken into use. This means that the reels are not heavily constructed and will suffer damage if mishandled. It should also be borne in mind that the cable wound onto the reels will be of high value.

- Reels of cable should be stowed in the fore-and-aft line of the vessel and should be chocked with timber, appropriate to the size of the reels, to prevent movement of the reels and chafage.

- Small reels which are, by their nature, more strongly constructed, may be block stowed with the flat surface of one against the flat surface of the next. Such a block stowage must be tight and compact without any vacant space. The block should be adequately timbered and secured by the use of appropriate lashing materials.

- Larger dimension reels should be stowed and secured individually. Large reels sometimes have cradles fitted, in which event stowage is made somewhat easier. If the reels are not fitted with cradles than either a suitable timber cradle must be constructed or wedges of suitable size must be fitted to prevent the reels from rolling in the fore-and-aft line.

- The rules with regard to lashing, for the prevention of sliding and tipping over, must always be followed.

- Reels of cable must not be stowed with their axes in the fore-and-aft line, like coils of steel. If they are stowed like coils extensive damage might easily result. This is because when slight movement of the reels occurs in the fore-and-aft line, in the direction of their axis, the rims of adjacent reels, which might be only a few centimetres in breadth, will move out of alignment and the reels will then be free to roll athwartships and cause damage to the cables - very expensive.

REELS OF PAPER

Paper carried as reels comes in a number of forms and a variety of reel sizes. The type of paper ranges from fibre board or liner board which might be quite thick and is used in the construction of cartons, through newsprint and other printing paper which might be very thin, to tissue paper which is delicate. Sizes range from small reels of diameter and height less than 1m in the case of printing paper, up to possibly more than 1.5 m diameter and 2 m high reels in the case of tissue paper. All reels are provided with minimal packaging which might be in the form of clingfilm or shrink wrap polythene in the case of tissue paper reels or a liner board wrapping with head disks glued in place for other types of paper.

- Whatever the size or packaging, reels of paper are susceptible to contact damage and wetting damage.

- Reels must be stowed upon a flat smooth surface covered with paper and a block of reels must be protected on all sides. The most appropriate stowage is in a box-shaped compartment.

- When stowing reels in other shaped compartments, or together with other break-bulk items, care must be exercised to ensure that the surface on to which the reels are being stowed is horizontal, level and stable, and that the block is adequately secured on all sides. Such securing arrangements might include the fitting of fencing, in the form of gratings, plywood and timber, around the open faces of the block stowage with lashings of wire, webbing or fibre rope, as appropriate, around the block and led to bulkheads or the ship's side structure.

- It must be remembered that the reels are highly susceptible to damage and therefore the lashings must not touch the reels and the fencing must be constructed and arranged such that the possibility of chafage and rubbing of the reels is minimised. Fitting of additional soft packing might be appropriate in some cases.

TANKS, VESSELS, ETC.

Tanks, vessels and other such items might have no lashing points, might be offered for shipment without any form of cradle or support structure and might have an external coating which must not be contacted by the securing arrangements. It might, therefore, be appropriate to have discussions with shippers' representatives in order to establish how best to secure the items. The pieces might have flanges or support feet and it might be possible to use such fittings for the attachment of lashings or to put timber chocking against, but it might not. In the absence of any appropriate fittings a timber framework or crib, combining cradles and support structures must be constructed beneath and around the base. Lashings can then be fitted to the support structure and then, where and how appropriate, to the item itself.

In the CSS Code the method of securing portable tanks and receptacles having no securing points is by the use of loops around the unit such that both ends of each loop are secured to the same side of the unit. Each unit must, of course, be fitted with a balanced number of loops leading variously to port and to starboard. A loop will prevent the item of cargo from shifting in the direction away from the lashing securing point and therefore such loop lashings can be counted in the evaluation of securing arrangements. The alternative of leading lashings over the top of the cargo unit in the form of a round-turn, such that the two ends of the lashing are secured to lashing points on either side of the unit, will increase the friction as a result of their vertical component but it is likely that the possibility of movement of the unit within such lashings will not be eliminated. For this reason such round-turn lashings cannot be included in any evaluation calculations.

- Tanks, vessels and the like are often longer than they are broad. This being the case they should be stowed in the fore-and-aft direction.

- The weight of the item should be borne in mind and calculations should be carried out to ensure that the loading rate in way of the base structure, be it cradles or foot supports, does not exceed the maximum permissible loading of the deck or tank-top. Timber dunnage should be used to spread the load.

- When lifting points are used as securing points, first establish that those lifting points can be used for lashings and establish their strength and the arc over which they can be used. If they only have strength in the athwartships line they cannot be used for lashing in the fore-and-aft line.

SUITABILITY FOR SHIPMENT

The advice given in the sub-sections above, although given for specific types of commodity, can be used for the stowage and securing of other items not listed. Care must always be exercised when taking a shipment on board for carriage to its destination. However, the suitability of the items of cargo for shipment to destination must always be borne in mind. If the items of cargo cannot be satisfactorily stowed and adequately secured on board the vessel, in a way which will not lead to the items of cargo suffering damage, then those items are not suitable for shipment on board the particular vessel and therefore they should not be taken. It is better to decline to carry cargo than to carry it knowing that it is likely to sustain damage during the voyage.

STEEL PRODUCTS

Steel products being stowed in the hold of a bulk carrier.

Steel products can be divided into two types; those which are packaged or wrapped and those which are shipped without any form of packaging. Generally speaking, those products which are wrapped are finished or semi-finished products and those which are not packaged are unfinished products. Some types of steel products, for example coils of steel sheets, can be either finished and wrapped or unfinished and not wrapped, whereas other types, for example billets, are only unfinished. The main types of products are described below.

Coils of Steel Sheets

Hot rolled steel sheets are unfinished and therefore hot rolled coils are not wrapped and are merely secured in coil form by steel bands. Cold reduced steel sheeting, galvanised steel sheeting and any other sheeting with a surface preparation are finished products and therefore cold reduced coils, etc. are packaged with an inner water-shed paper liner and with outer steel sheet wrappers, all held in place by steel bands.

Top-Hat Coils

A top-hat coil, sometimes called a stillage, is a coil of steel sheet which is placed, with its eye vertical, onto a timber pallet base or timber rickers which have been nailed to form a strong timber base, such that it looks something like a top-hat. The coil will be of cold reduced sheeting, galvanised steel sheeting or any other finished steel sheeting and is therefore packaged with an inner waterproof paper liner and with outer steel wrappers, all held in place by steel bands and with further steel bands to hold the coil onto the pallet base or rickers.

Cut Steel Sheets

As with coils of steel sheets, bundles of cut steel sheets might be of hot rolled, unfinished, sheets, or of cold reduced, galvanised or surface finished sheeting. Bundles of hot rolled sheets, which might for example be diamond plate, will be secured by longitudinal and transverse steel bands and might have transversely aligned timber rickers. Finished sheets will be packaged with an inner water-shed paper liner over which there will be steel sheet wrappers, the package will be fitted onto transversely aligned timber bearers and all will be held in place by steel bands.

Steel Plates
Plates are of thickness, generally speaking, above about 3 mm and up to possibility 250 mm. They are unfinished and therefore not wrapped. They are sometimes secured by steel bands into bundles, although thicker plates are carried individually. They can be small, of dimensions 1 m x 2 m or larger up to 12 m x 3 m, or even larger on occasion.

Steel Slabs, Billets and Blooms
These are unfinished products which will be heated and rolled to form plates or bars, etc. They are not wrapped and are carried either singly or in bundles, depending upon their size.

Structural Steels
This category includes beams, angles, flats, channels and other shapes of bar. These are mostly unfinished and carried in unwrapped bundles, but finished and coated sections are often carried either singly or in bundles.

Merchant Bars
These are small cross-section bars; round, square, channels, T-bars etc., which are for the most part unfinished and therefore carried in unwrapped bundles, but sometimes they are semi-finished bright bars or are oiled, and are then wrapped in some form of sheeting which might be hessian or synthetic.

Pipes and Tubes
These come in a range of types and sizes, some formed into bundles and others carried individually. Most are unfinished and therefore shipped without packaging but small section tubing, which is often called hollow section, is a semi-finished product and is often carried oiled and wrapped in either hessian or synthetic sheeting.

Wire rod
Wire rod is sometimes carried in coil form and sometimes in cut lengths in bundles. Included in this category is reinforcing wire rod, or re-bar, which might be profiled for use in concrete structures. It is an unfinished product and therefore not packaged, being merely retained in coil or bundle form by either steel bands or wire ties.

Railway Iron
Rails are loaded at specialised ports individually and unwrapped.

All steel products are, by their very nature, heavy and require an amount of pre-planning before loading can commence.

- The cargo compartment must be clean and dry and a pre-loading inspection of the compartment might be carried out on behalf of the shipper of the cargo before loading begins. Such a pre-loading inspection might include an inspection and test of the weather deck hatch covers.

- A stowage plan must be drawn up showing the arrangement of the cargo on board, and strength and stability calculations should be completed in order to demonstrate that the maximum shear force and bending moments are not exceeded and the vessel's stability is satisfactory for the entire voyage. Calculations should be completed with regard to the distribution of the cargo to establish that the maximum permissible tank-top or deck loading is not exceeded.

- Sufficient quantities of the appropriate types of dunnage materials should be available for use.

- All of this pre-planning should be completed before loading is begun.

COILS OF STEEL SHEET

Coils are shipped in a range of weights up to around 30 tonnes and in a range of sizes. Coils should be stowed as follows:

- Coils should be stowed on the round with their axis in the fore-and-aft line of the vessel in athwartships rows, on lines of flat-board timber dunnage laid athwartships on the tank-top, preferably laid above inner bottom transverse stiffening members.

- Each coil should be stowed hard up against coils to port and to starboard and wedges should be inserted against the inboard bilge of each coil and preferably nailed to the tank-top timber dunnage. Timber dunnage should be fitted between outboard coils and the ship's structure.

- If the coils are to be stowed in a single tier only, the last coil to be placed into stowage should be positioned as a locking coil, at a higher level so as to act like a wedge, in the space remaining in the middle of the row which must be of breadth about one-third of the diameter of the coil such that the locking coil will tend to force the coils to port and to starboard outboard. The locking coil will sink a little as the stowage settles during the voyage. The locking coil should be lashed to the two coils supporting it.

- If there is a longer space left in the middle of the row then that space should be split in two by moving middle coils and then two locking coils should be fitted and lashed in place.

- If second and third tiers of coils are to be carried those second and third tier coils should be stowed in the cantlines of the coils in the tier below. Top tier coils should be secured to the coils of the next tier below by the use of wires set tight by rigging screws or by metal strapping bands, tensioned correctly.

- Void spaces within the upper tiers should be avoided but if spaces are unavoidable then more timber dunnage should be put in place to ensure that the coil stowage is ridged and such that the timber chocking will not be displaced during the voyage.

- Each transverse row should be separated from the next by a gap of at least 150 mm to prevent contact between coils in adjacent rows because this would cause damage. Similarly, end rows should be kept well clear of bulkheads. Timber may be inserted between adjacent rows and against end bulkheads if thought appropriate.

- When loading coils of steel sheets the deck or tank-top strength must not be exceeded and the height to which coils can be stowed, depending upon their weight, must not be exceeded; this height of stowage is often given in the ship's Cargo Securing Manual. Guidance on stowage height and tank-top strength calculations is given in a later part of this section.

Diagrams showing correct stowage and lashing systems can be found in the ship's Cargo Securing Manual.

TOP-HAT COILS

Top-hat coils are shipped in a range of sizes and weights, although not as large and heavy as coils on the round, and are of weight up to about 15 tonnes. Great care should taken when placing top-hat coils into stowage because it is often the case that the timber base is wider than is the diameter of the coil. This means that when two top-hat coils are placed such that their base units are hard up against each other the coils upon those bases are not touching. These products should be stowed as follows:

- It should be ensured that the stevedores' handling equipment is suitable for the size and weight of the product so that no damage is sustained by the timber pallets. If damage is sustained by the timber-work the unit should be returned ashore for repair and not placed into stowage because an unsound base will lead to movement of the stowage during the ocean passage and damage to coils.

- The units should be placed directly on to the tank-top or deck plating although timber dunnage should be used as and where appropriate to level the tank-top or deck such that the top-hat coils are stowed vertical and level one with another and such that the ground onto which the coils are placed is firm. The units should be stowed in athwartships rows hard up against one another. Coils in adjacent rows should also be hard up against one another in the fore-and-aft line.

- Timber chocking should be used between adjacent coils in the fore-and-aft line and in the athwartships line such that the coils are chocked one against another and such that the stowage as a whole is a solid unit. Flat board dunnage should be used to connect vertical chocks to eliminate, so far as possible, the likelihood of those chocks falling away during the voyage.

- Top-hat coils placed into a second and third tier must be placed squarely onto a coil in the lower tier and those second and third tier coils should be similarly chocked against adjacent coils. Staggering of coils in second and third tiers should be avoided because damage to lower tier coils will result.

- Outboard to port and to starboard substantial timber shores should be set up between the outboard coils and the ship's side structure to support those outboard coils over the full height of the stowage.

- Open athwartships faces should be secured by a combination of wire lashings led around groups of coils and to lashing points or ship's structure and large section timber dunnage or timber gratings in a fashion similar to that used to secure blocks of break-bulk cargo, and clearly of adequately substantial nature.

- Lashing wires should be set up around the blocks of coils to tie them together; such wires should be led around lengths of large section timber such that the wires do not come into contact with the coils.

PACKAGES AND BUNDLES

These includes all products which have square ends and sides, including cut sheets, small plates, small diameter pipes, hollow section, etc. These should be stowed in stacks hard up against each other either in athwartships lines in the case of smaller dimension products such as cut sheets, or in the fore-and-aft direction in the case of bundles of hollow section and the like.

- Dunnage should be used to level the tank-top or deck plating as and where appropriate and to level the stowage in way of intermediate tiers. Timber should also be used at intermediate tiers to lock adjacent stacks together.

- The packages or bundles should be stowed hard up against each other such that there is no void space within the stowage. If spaces are unavoidable, timber chocks should be fitted to prevent movement of the cargo.

- Outboard to port and to starboard, and adjacent to the end bulkheads appropriate timber chocking should be fitted to prevent any of the steel products coming into contact with the ship's structure and to ensure a tight and secure stowage.

- It is often the case that stowages of packages and/or bundles require no securing by wires or steel bands because the products are adequately chocked against movement being hard against end bulkheads and side structures. However, when there is an open face of smaller dimension packages at one end of the stowage that face will require securing to prevent movement during the voyage. Securing should be by a combination of wire lashings led to lashing points or ship's structure used in conjunction with large section timber dunnage, timber pallet boards or timber gratings, in a fashion similar to that used to secure blocks of break-bulk cargo, and clearly of adequately substantial nature.

BUNDLES OF BARS

For this sub-section reinforcing bars, merchant bars and small diameter tubes and pipes are included. These bundles are likely to be irregular and cannot therefore be stowed in regular tiers.

- The bundles should be stowed in the fore-and-aft line of the vessel upon timber dunnage laid athwartships on the tank-top or deck plating.

- The bundles should be stowed compactly so that there are no void spaces within the stowage.

- Timber dunnage should be used as necessary to level the stowage and outboard to port and to starboard so that the bundles are kept clear of the ship's structure.

STEEL SLABS, BILLETS, BLOOMS AND PLATES

These are heavy items which are often of irregular dimensions and will need particular care when positioning in stowage, and will require a lot of dunnaging.

- Sufficient timber dunnage should be used on the tank-top or deck plating to satisfactorily spread the load of the products.

- Plates may be stowed either athwartships or longitudinally but in such a manner as to produce a tight, even and level stowage with a minimum of void space.

- Ample timber dunnage should be used within the stowage, as chocking in void spaces, between plates to level the stowage and around its perimeter to prevent contact between the steel products and the ship's structure.

- Stacks of plates should be avoided unless such stacks are surrounded and supported by other stacks of plates that can be tied together by timber dunnage at intermediate levels. stowing with plates overlapping each other will produce a tight and secure block of cargo which is more stable and therefore less likely to shift during the voyage.

Steel slabs present their own specific needs. These products weigh up to 20 tonnes, are of thickness around 250 mm and dimensions of 6 m x 1.2 m or more. They should be stowed in a similar fashion to that for plates, as given above. That is, briefly, with ample dunnage on the tank-top (in line with transverse floors), aligned mostly fore-and-aft, staggered so that they overlap one another and with others athwartships to form a good stable locking stow, winged out over the hopper tanks of a bulk carrier, and with plenty of good quality, substantial timber between the tiers and as chocking in void spaces between adjacent slabs. The principal being to produce an interlocking block stowage which will not shift.

CALIFORNIA BLOCK STOWAGE

California block stow.

An alternative stowage arrangement which significantly reduces stevedoring costs is known as the "California block stow". This arrangement requires that the slabs be stowed squarely on top of each other to produce a stowage of many individual vertical stacks of slabs. Timber dunnage is used on the tank-top and between each tier, and as chocking between the stacks. Finally, steel bands are used around each stack to secure the slabs together. This method of stowage is only acceptable for vessels with box-shaped holds, and only then when the stowage extends to both port and starboard sides, is sufficiently chocked against the hold side plating and throughout the full breadth and length of the stowage. This method cannot be used in the holds of other vessels because it cannot be adequately secured and the slabs are therefore likely to shift and cause severe damage to the structure of the cargo compartment when the vessel rolls and pitches in the seaway.

STRUCTURAL STEEL

This might be in bundles but if the sections are of large dimension they will be loose.

- These products should be stowed in the fore-and-aft line of the vessel on timber dunnage laid athwartships on the tank-top or deck plating and timber dunnage should be laid athwartships between each tier in line with the timber on the tank-top or deck.

- The products should be stowed on their flanges so that their webs are vertical. This will avoid damage to the webs caused by over-stowed cargo.

- The stowage should be tight and compact and when space between the products is unavoidable timber dunnage should be used to chock the steel against movement.

- If it is necessary, because of the dimensions of the cargo compartment or the steel, for part of the cargo to be stowed in the athwartships line other cargo should be stowed outboard to port and to starboard, either structural steel products or other suitable cargo, and the aligned steel should be stowed against that other cargo with adequate timber chocking between the two stowages.

- Blocks of structural steel often require lashing in addition to timber chocking. Such securing should be by steel wire of suitable size, led round upper tier products and down to appropriate securing points or ship's structure.

PIPES

Pipes are shipped either in bundles or loose. Bundles of pipes should be stowed in the fore-and-aft line in a manner similar to that described for packages and bundles, above. Large dimension pipes should be stowed in the fore-and-aft line and never in the athwartships line. Ample dunnage and lashing materials will be needed.

- As with other steel products timber dunnage should be laid athwartships on the tank-top or deck plating so far as possible in line with under deck athwartships stiffening members.

- Steel pipes will be stowed in a number of tiers. Second tier pipes will normally be stowed in the cantlines of the lower tier pipes. Subsequent tiers are similarly stowed such that a sort of brick pattern is formed.

Whenever possible only pipes of the same diameter should be stowed together. This will ensure that the stowage is tight and neat and without any space between pipes in each tier. Such a stowage of same size pipes will, however, require timbering outboard to port and to starboard and such timbering should be substantial and strong. Skimping of such chocking is likely to lead to collapse of the stowage.

- Securing of the top tier or upper tiers should be completed using wire rope of adequate and the pipes in order to prevent damage to the pipes and to give the wire a better grip on the pipes' surface.

- Where pipes of different diameter have to be stowed together all gaps between adjacent pipes should be chocked by the use of ample quantities of timber dunnage.

- When pipes with special characteristics, such as a paint coating or end fitting, are to be loaded the shippers should be contacted for information with regard to their stowage requirements, and additional information from local surveyors might be necessary in order to achieve a satisfactory and appropriate stowage for the pipes.

WIRE ROD

As mentioned earlier, wire rod is shipped in either coils or in bundles. Bundles will be stowed as described for bundles of bars, above. Coils of wire which have been formed correctly with correctly applied securing bands are fairly ridged and can be stacked satisfactorily. However, coils made up with slack bands will be floppy and cannot therefore be stacked satisfactorily.

- The coils should be stowed in athwartships rows with their axies in the fore-and-aft line of the vessel upon timber dunnage laid on the tank-top or deck plating in the athwartships line.

- The coils will be stowed in a number of tiers. Second, third, etc. tiers should be stowed in the cantlines of the lower tier coils to form a tight stowage.

- Adjacent athwartships rows of coils should be stowed hard up against each other to form a solid block of coils.

- Timber dunnage should be used outboard to port and to starboard and adjacent to end bulkheads to support the block of coils and to prevent contact between coils and ship's structure.

- If the block of coils does not fill the cargo compartment and an open face is left, that face must be secured by the use of wire lashings in conjunction with timber or pallets or fencing in a fashion similar to that used to secure blocks of break-bulk cargo.

TANK-TOP STRENGTH CALCULATIONS

Bulk carriers are commonly used for the carriage of steel products and even though some bulk carriers have strong tank-top structures and high maximum permissible tank-top loadings care must be taken to load steel products to an acceptable height, with sufficient timber dunnage laid out on the tank-top plating, in order that the maximum permissible loading rate is not exceeded. When the cargo includes steel plates, bundles of bars or steel billets the calculations are relatively easy and the spacing of the timber dunnage can be easily assessed.
However, for steel coils the calculations are not so straightforward and a great deal of research has been done to establish how best to stow coils without damaging the tank-top structure.

When a steel coil is placed on the tank-top plating without any timber dunnage, for example during loading and discharging, the contact area is very small and therefore the loading in way of that contact area is large, possibly over 70 tonnes/m^2 for a 25-tonne coil. The weight of the coil will, of course, be transferred outward and down, through the steel plating of the tank-top into the longitudinal and athwartships stiffening members within the double-bottom tank below and therefore, although the point loading might exceed the maximum permissible loading given in the ship's documents, structural damage will not result from the weight of that single coil while the vessel is stationary and not rolling in the seaway. When timber dunnage is laid athwarthships on the tank-top the weight of the coil is spread further to port and to starboard into the ship's structure and therefore the actual loading rate is reduced.

Classification Society naval architects are often asked to what height coils of steel sheet of a given size and weight can be safely stowed on the tank-top plating of a given vessel. In order to answer the question the naval architects will carry out calculations using details of the coils, various arrangements of dunnage, a range of numbers of tiers, the area of structure taking the weight and certain factors, and then produce tables giving, for a range of coil weights and sizes, and a range of tier heights, whether or not the coils can safely be stowed on top of a range of arrangements of dunnage. For example, on board a particular vessel with a tank-top strength of 22 tonnes/m² it might be acceptable for coils of weight 15.0 tonnes and width 2.5 m to be stowed three high on 4 lengths of good quality timber dunnage, but not acceptable if those 15.0-tonne coils were of width 1.5 m. However, the tables would, perhaps, also show that the 15.0-tonne coils of width 1.5 m can safely be stowed three high if 8 lengths of good quality timber dunnage are provided for each athwartship row. Such tables produced by Classification Societies will, of course, be applicable only to the vessel for which they were produced, and the requirements with regard to dunnaging must be strictly adhered to.

Experience has shown that when no specific calculations have been carried out for the vessel, a simple rule can be used which is - *ensure that the weight imposed on the tank-top in way of bottom tier coils does not exceed about 30 tonnes to 35 tonnes.*

This can be transposed into a simple rule, with regard to the weight and height ratio of coils, as shown in Table 5.

Weight of Coils	Height of Coils
Up to about 10 tonnes	3
Up to about 15 tonnes	2
More than 15 tonnes	1

Table 5 - Weight and height ratio of steel coils.

Clearly, if coils of a range of sizes are to be loaded together, with larger coils in the bottom tier and smaller coils on top, a compromise must be found such that the bottom tier coils do not impose more than 30 tonnes onto the tank-top plating.

This simple rule and the table are based upon the tank-top strength being unknown, or not high, and there being only two or three lines of timber dunnage. Clearly, as can be seen above, if more lines of good quality timber dunnage are provided heavier coils can be stowed to a greater height, without overstressing the tank-top structures.

It is often the case that calculations for coil stowages are carried out by the naval architects during the design stage and therefore a table of weight and height ratios is given on the ship's plans and in the vessel's trim and stability booklet. Also, such a table might be given in the ship's Cargo Securing Manual. Such a table should be complied with unless the stowage of the coils being loaded cannot be matched to any arrangement in the table, in which case other calculations need to be completed. If on the other hand, substantially more timber dunnage is to be used than is allowed for in the table it might be permissible to stow coils to a height greater than given in the table. It must always be remembered that if a departure from anything in the vessel's Cargo Securing Manual is to be contemplated, the basic rules of good seamanship practice must always be observed, and if in doubt call for assistance.

When a bulk carrier is chartered for a single voyage to carry steel products there will generally be a description of the vessel within one of the clauses of the charter party and that description might include maximum permissible tank-top loadings. It is recommended that the following should be borne in mind.

- Many bulk carriers, as mentioned above, will be designed to carry heavy cargo in alternate holds, with the other holds empty, and might be assigned maximum permissible loadings for the loaded holds which are higher than the maximum permissible loading rates assigned to those holds which would remain empty.

For example, 22 tonnes/m^2 for the loaded holds (nos.1, 3, 5, etc.) and 14 tonnes/m^2 for the holds which would remain empty (nos.2, 4, etc.). Such vessels might also be assigned a second set of tank-top loading rates for the homogenous loaded condition (that is with cargo, beit bulk cargo or break-bulk cargo, in all holds), and that loading rate might be 14 tonnes/m^2, as given for the empty holds despite the 22 tonne/m^2 rate for the alternate loaded holds. Both loading rates should be quoted in the charter party.

- When a table or list of weight and stowage height ratios for steel coil loading is given in the Cargo Securing Manual or in any of the ship's documents, that table should be given in the charter party in order to avoid any confusion as to how high coils can be stowed.

- If there is any other information in the Cargo Securing Manual or ship's documents with regard to the stowage of steel products, that also should be given in the ship's description.

HEAVY-LIFT ITEMS AND PROJECT CARGO

Project cargo.

These items are often of high value and great weight. They may have delicate parts which must not be contacted and they may or may not be suitable for carriage on deck, which will undoubtedly mean wetting by rain and sea water. They must be fitted with lifting points and lashing points which are of adequate strength and positioned in appropriate places. The carriage of these items should be planned in great detail from origin to destination. Of particular interest here is the planning of the stowage and securing.

VOYAGE PLANNING

The voyage must be planned in order to ensure that the piece of cargo can be safely transported from origin to destination, and the points to be borne in mind are as follows:

- The vessel must be able to safely berth alongside at the load port and at the destination port, and safely take on board and finally land the item, bearing in mind; mooring arrangements, stability requirements, crane capacity and crane outreach.

- The load port and destination port must be suitable for the carrying vessel. They must also be suitable for carrying vehicles, that is the dockside must be suitable in terms of strength and accessibility.

- Sufficient lashing materials and dunnaging materials must be provided on board after appropriate calculations have been carried out to determine the requirements, see Pre-Planning below.

- Professional securing contractors should be employed, if appropriate, to carry out the necessary calculations and to secure the items in place.

PRE-PLANNING

The shippers of the cargo should provide the master, or representative of the carrier, with information about the cargo so that the stowage and securing can be properly planned in advance.

The information should include the following:

- A general description of the cargo.
- The gross mass of the item or of each item if there are more than one.
- The principal dimensions of the item or items and, if possible, scale drawings.
- The location of the centre of gravity of each item.
- Particulars of the bedding area of the cargo units and details of any precautions with regard to the bedding of the item(s).
- Details of lifting points or slinging positions and if possible information on how best to lift each item.
- Details of securing points, including their strength and radius of strength.

Some heavy lift items are not fitted with any form of bedding arrangements apart from foundations or legs upon which they would ordinarily stand. Others will be completely cased in timber-work and will be provided with a timber floor which is capable of taking and spreading the weight of the item, whilst others will be fitted with cradles of limited strength. Information about the construction of base units is required so that appropriate arrangements can be made on board to adequately and appropriately bed and support the item.

- The lifting points should be fitted symmetrically on either side of the centre of gravity and should also be fitted with sufficient spread, to be not less than half the length of the unit, to enable safe and level lifting of the unit without the use of additional sling/lengthening equipment. Lifting points should be clearly marked.
- Securing points should be of adequate strength and their minimum strength must be advised. Lashing points should be so constructed as to have a wide arc of strength because lashings will not necessarily be led directly in line with the plane of the lashing point. All lashing points should be suitably marked.
- The strength and base area of any cradles, foundations or bedding provided must be known in order to establish what else is needed for the support of the load atop the vessel's hatch cover, deck or tank-top, bearing in mind the maximum permissible load.

STOWAGE PLANNING

When details of the base structure or cradles is known a suitable stowage location can be chosen and suitable bedding material can be ordered. With regard to the stowage location the following points should be borne in mind.

- Cargo stowed on the weather deck or hatch covers will be exposed to rain and sea water wetting and to the wind. Only items which the shippers have confirmed are suitable to withstand exposure to the elements may be stowed on deck.
- The accelerations generated by the vessel are less lower down at the mid-part of the vessel

than they are further from that centre of motion. Heavy items of cargo should, when possible, be stowed close to the vessel's centre of motion.

- Distribution of the weight of the item should be considered together with the maximum permissible loading of the deck or tank-top on to which the piece is to be stowed. The extent to which the weight of the item must be spread must then be calculated and from that the bedding requirements can be assessed.

- The purpose of bedding is to provide a solid base onto which the item can be placed and secured down onto and to distribute the weight of the unit evenly over the stowage area so as to keep loading below the maximum permissible loading rate. Also, bedding provides a high friction co-efficient between the cargo unit and the deck or tank-top.

- Bedding materials include flat board dunnage, square section timber beams, especially manufactured platforms and steel beams. The most appropriate type of platform material should be used bearing in mind the required area of weight distribution, the weight of the item to be carried and the strength of any cradles, foundations or legs.

- Cradles, foundations, legs, etc. might be designed for transport by road or rail, or for installation on site, but might be of insufficient strength for sea transport. Thus, the item of cargo itself might require additional support arrangements in the form of timber and/or steel brackets and buttresses. If there is any doubt about the strength of cradles, etc. additional support should be provided, below the cargo item.

- Heavy-lift items should be stowed in the fore-and-aft line of the vessel.

SECURING PLANNING

When the detail of a piece of heavy-lift or project cargo is known, calculations can be carried out to determine how many lashings are required to adequately secure the cargo against movement. Also, the required distribution of those lashings can be assessed. Points to be borne in mind during such an assessment are as follows:

- The method of securing should be decided upon, that is by the use of wire lashings, chain lashings, or whatever. Because different materials have different characteristics with regard to flexibility and elasticity, all lashings should be of the same make-up, that is all wire lashings, all chain lashings, or all chains with wire grommets, if applicable. If a combination of types of lashing is used, those with low elasticity will take more load than those which have a higher elasticity.

- Calculations should be carried out to determine how many lashings of the type decided upon are needed by use of the Advanced Calculation Method or, if insufficient information is available, by use of the Rule-of-Thumb method.

- Lashings should be fitted in an arrangement which will withstand transverse and longitudinal forces which may give rise to sliding or tipping of the item.

- The optimum lashing angle to act against sliding is about 25° to the horizontal, whereas the optimum lashing angle to act against tipping is in the range from 45° to 60° to the horizontal.

- If necessary, additional lashing points should be welded to the ship's structure in appropriate places. The surface in way of where the lashing point is to be welded should be in suitable condition and welding should only take place in accordance with accepted hot work procedures. Welding to ship's structural members such as frames, and welding in way of fuel tanks, should be forbidden, unless Class approval is obtained.

- Where appropriate, welded steel sea fastening or dogs should be considered. Sea fastenings are usually made from steel profiles such as H-girders welded to the deck plating or tank-top close to the base structure of the item to allow chocking of the unit by the use of timber wedges or timber blocks. The rules for welding as given above should be followed.

- Where appropriate, timber shores and buttresses should be fitted against the sides and ends of items of cargo and against adjacent items of cargo or against ship's structural members, to support the item of cargo against movement. Such shores and buttresses should be constructed from good quality timber of adequate cross-section; small dimension timber will give way and bend and prove to be of no use.

- If the item of cargo has no securing points, or an insufficient number of securing points, lashings must be secured in loops which pass around the item. Such loops should be arranged such that both ends of the lashing are secured on the same side of the unit. Thus, an even number of opposing lashings must be fitted.

- If calculations are carried out by professional securing contractors they will be able to calculate the strength of sea fastenings, timber shores, buttresses, etc., and the strength of those arrangements can be taken into account when deciding upon the overall lashing requirements.

USE OF SEA FASTENINGS

Sea fastenings used to secure concrete mats and a float onto a barge.

There are some items of project cargo which have no lashing points and no means of applying lashings to the cargo. Concrete structures and flat sided tanks are two examples. Such items can be adequately secured by the use of sea fastenings and timber shores and buttresses alone.

Steel dogs can be welded at appropriate places around the base of the unit and fitted with wooden wedges or square timber blocks to prevent sliding of the unit in both the athwartships line and in the fore-and-aft line. Timber shores and buttresses can be fitted to a high level against the sides and ends of the unit to prevent it from tipping over.

RO-RO CARGO ITEMS

Ro-ro container trailer secured on trestle.

Ro-ro cargo items include all the various types of commercial vehicles for road transport, roll trailers and other pieces which are driven aboard the vessel. Commercial vehicles include semi-trailers without a towing tractor unit, combination vehicles comprising a tractor unit with one or more towed vehicles, and other commercial vehicles which are not articulated. Roll trailers are used within port areas and on board ro-ro vessels for the carriage of large, awkward or heavy pieces of cargo via the stern or side door. Other pieces include caravans, boats, trailers, etc. and construction or road building machinery, farm machinery, etc., either wheeled or on tracks. These three basic types will be dealt with separately.

ROAD VEHICLES

There are extensive recommendations and requirements with regard to the safe carriage of road vehicles aboard ro-ro vessels. The recommendations and requirements can be divided into four parts, those applying to the basic standards of acceptance of the vehicle, lashing equipment on board, stowage and securing of the vehicle and consideration of the voyage.

Basic Standards for Acceptance of Vehicles

All vehicles should be inspected before they are loaded to ensure that they are in a seaworthy condition and suitable for carriage on the intended voyage. This means that the vehicle must be suitable for securing on board and must have adequate strength to withstand the rigours of the voyage, and the cargo on the vehicle must not shift during the voyage. The requirements are as follows:

- The cargo on the vehicle must be properly stowed and adequately secured such that it will not move during the voyage. Machinery on a flat-bed trailer must be properly secured as if it were on the deck of the vessel, pallets or other units within a box van must be adequately chocked and items of whatever type must be secured to the bed of a curtain-sided trailer; the side-curtains are not there to secure the cargo they are there to keep the rain out.

- The trailer should be fitted with an equal number of lashing points to each side in accordance with the following:-

  Gross vehicle mass 3.5 tonnes to 20 tonnes - 2 lashing points
  Gross vehicle mass 20 tonnes to 30 tonnes - 3 lashing points
  Gross vehicle mass 30 tonnes to 40 tonnes - 4 lashing points

- Each lashing point should have a strength, without permanent deformation, of at least 120 kN or 12 tonnes. The lashing points should be fitted at suitable places on the vehicle so as to ensure efficient restraint of the vehicle by the lashings, such that the lashing point is capable of transferring the forces from the lashings to the chassis of the vehicle, and such that lashings can be readily and safely attached.

- When a semi-trailer is shipped unaccompanied, that is without a tractor unit, its front end will be supported on a trestle placed below the chassis close to the rear of the draw plate. That area of the chassis should be suitably re-enforced for the purpose and that area should be clearly marked.

- Some times it will be necessary to jack-up the chassis in way of the axles, such jacking-up points on the chassis should be suitably strengthened.

Lashing Equipment On Board

Ro-ro vessels designed for the carriage of vehicles will have their decks laid out and fitted for the purpose and they will have on board suitable lashing and stowage equipment. The primary items are as follows:

- The decks will be laid out in lanes with securing points fitted along each lane. Those securing points should be not more than 2.5 m apart in the fore-and-aft direction and the lane should not be less than 2.8 m, nor more than 3.0 m wide.

- The lashing points should have a strength without permanent deformation of not less than 120 kN or 12 tonnes. If the securing points are designed to accommodate more than one lashing then the strength of the lashing points should be 120 kN times the number of lashings it can accommodate.

- Lashings should be of chain and should have strength, without permanent deformation, of not less than 120 kN or 12 tonnes.

- Lashings should be designed with a hook or other devices for attachment to the vehicle and an appropriate fitting to engage the deck securing point. They should also be fitted with an attachment which allows for initial tightening after attachment and further tightening if they become slack during the voyage.

- There should be sufficient trestles for the supporting of semi-trailers and sufficient jacks for the support of chassis in way of axles.

Stowage and Securing of the Vehicle

Vehicles should be stowed in the fore-and-aft line of the vessel with sufficient space around the vehicle for examinations to be carried out during the voyage. Each vehicle should be adequately and properly secured for the intended voyage. The primary points to be borne in mind are as follows:

- Only proper securing points on vehicles should be used for lashing purposes. Lashings should not be attached to lamp brackets, bumpers, side-guards, etc, unless they have been specifically designed for use as securing points on the vehicle.

- Only one lashing should be attached to any one securing point. Lashings are most effective on vehicles when they are made at an angle with the deck of between 30° and 60°. When these optimum angles cannot be achieved, additional lashings might be required.

- Lashings should be fitted such that on each side of the vehicle there is at least one lashing leading forward, one lashing leading aft and one, so far as possible leading athwartships.

- Lashings should not be crossed from side to side; they should lead from the lashing point outboard and down to the deck fitting.

- The master should take into consideration the weather conditions likely to be encountered during the intended voyage and should decide upon the number of lashings to be fitted to each side of each vehicle.

- Consideration should be taken into account with regard to the position of individual vehicles on board when deciding upon the number of lashings to be fitted. Vehicles stowed right forward or right aft and outboard to port or to starboard may require the fitting of additional lashings in view of the large accelerations which will be experienced by vehicles at those locations.

- The parking breaks should be applied and locked and vehicles with diesel engines should not be left in gear during the voyage.

- The front end of the chassis of semi-trailers should be supported by a trestle positioned such that it does not restrict the connection of the fifth wheel to the kingpin. Landing legs should be lifted clear of the deck.

- Road vehicles should be secured in such a way that they are kept as static as possible by not allowing free play in the suspension system. Compressed air suspension systems may lose air and therefore the air pressure should be released on vehicles fitted on such a system when necessary. If the air pressure is not released, the vehicle should be jacked-up to prevent any slackening of the lashings which would result from air leakage.

Consideration of the Voyage

A cargo of road vehicles is, basically no different from any other cargo when it comes to actions to be taken during the voyage. These are as follows:

- All vehicles must be properly stowed and properly and adequately secured before departure.

- All lashings should be examined at frequent and regular intervals and all lashings found to be slack should be re-tightened.

- Trestles and jacks should also be examined to ensure they are properly positioned.

- The load of each vehicle should, so far as is possible, be examined to ensure that it is not moving on the vehicle. If movement of loads on vehicles is found re-securing of that cargo should be carried out. If adverse weather is predicted for a later part of the voyage additional lashings should be fitted to vehicles as appropriate.

ROLL TRAILERS

These trailers are specifically designed for use within port areas and on board ro-ro vessels and are not taken outside such areas. They are of length 20 ft, 30 ft, 40 ft and 42 ft, have small diameter solid rubber wheels at the rear on axles which do not have suspension and have a ridged support bar at the front, such that they are horizontal when set down on to that bar. At the front end they have a coupling mouth which accepts the gooseneck of specially designed tractor units such that the trailers can be lifted at their front end and towed without the tractor unit being actually coupled to the trailer. The trailers are used for the carriage of large, awkward or heavy pieces of cargo and have safe working loads in the range from 20 tonnes up to 200 tonnes.

The appropriate size and strength of trailer should be used for the particular piece of cargo or pieces of cargo which are being shipped.

- These trailers are fitted with numerous lashing points and the cargo must be appropriately and adequately secured to the trailer for handling on the deck and on board. The type and number of lashings will depend upon the cargo being carried. It might be appropriate to use wire rope, chains, webbing, or steel bands. Whichever type of lashing material is chosen, a suitable number of lashings, variously leading to the front, to the rear, and to both sides of the trailer should be fitted.

- The trailer should be stowed on board on the fore-and-aft line of the vessel. The support bar of the trailer should rest upon pieces of good quality timber dunnage or upon rubber matting supplied for the purpose.

- The trailer and its cargo should be secured to the deck of the vessel by either chain or wire rope. The required number of lashings should be calculated using the gross weight of the trailer, that is the trailer and the cargo, using either the Rule-of-Thumb or the Advanced Calculation Method.

- Lashings should be led from the trailer and from the cargo, as appropriate, to deck lashing points, variously leading forward, aft and athwartships. As mentioned before, lashings are most effective when they make an angle with the deck of between 30° and 60°. When the optimum angles cannot be achieved additional lashings might be required.

- As with other cargo, all lashings should be examined at frequent and regular intervals and all lashings found to be slack should be retightened.

- The load of each trailer should, so far as possible be examined to ensure that it is not moving on the trailer. If movement is found to be taking place all slack lashings should be re-tensioned and additional lashings to the trailer and/or the deck should be fitted.

- If adverse weather is predicted for a later part of the voyage additional lashings should be fitted to the trailer and to the cargo.

OTHER PIECES ON WHEELS OR TRACKS

Tracked vehicle secured on vehicle deck.

These include smaller items on wheels such as caravans, boats, trailers, etc; wheeled vehicles which are not road vehicles, such as building machinery and farming machinery, and lastly tracked vehicles and machinery. All of these items have one thing in common and that is that they do not have specifically designed lashing points. Some of them are very heavy and of strong and substantial construction, whilst others are light in weight and of light construction.

Caravans, Boats, Trailers, etc.
These are generally of light construction and might need to be supported from below as well as being tied down. Some points to bear in mind are as follows:

- It might be appropriate to fit lashings to axles, chassis members or towing bars. Other fittings such as bumpers, awning fittings, or other fittings which appear to be lashing points might not have sufficient strength for the requirements of a lashing point. Lashings must not cause damage to the fitting being used. Lashings should not be crossed from side to side; they should lead from the lashing point outboard and down to deck fittings.

- The suspension might be fairly light and therefore it might be necessary to fit chocks below chassis members or jacking points before fitting the lashings in order that those lashings will hold the vehicle or trailer down onto the chocks rather than acting against the suspension.

- The item might not have any brakes and therefore chocking around the wheels to prevent movement might be appropriate.

- If there are no points for lashings at all, such as on a boat, it will be necessary to lead lashings over the top of the piece. Before this is done the shippers should be contacted and asked for guidance as to where best to lead the lashings.

- Lashings of webbing or fibre rope might be more appropriate for some light construction pieces but chains or wire rope might be needed for other types.

- As with all lashing systems, lashings should be lead forward, aft and to both the port and the starboard sides of the vessel.

Building, Farming, etc. Machinery on Wheels
Such machines will be more heavily built with substantial chassis numbers, axles and tow bars, but they might also have light construction cabs or machinery housing extending to a considerable height. Points to be remembered with these vehicles are as follows:-

- These items are carried on ro-ro vessels and on conventional vessels both on and under deck.

- These vehicles are often of considerable weight and therefore the maximum permissible loading of the ro-ro deck, hatch cover, weather deck, or 'tween deck, whichever is in use, must be borne in mind. On a conventional vessel it will be necessary to spread the weight of the vehicle in way of the wheels by providing sufficient good quality timber dunnage beneath the wheels. It might be appropriate to construct timber gratings upon which the wheels can be landed.

- In order to restrict the movement of the vehicle it might be appropriate to fit chockings or wedges around each of the wheels and to fit timber chocking or jacks beneath the axles and jacking points.

- Calculations should be carried out using either the Rule-of-Thumb method or, if sufficient information is available, the Advanced Calculation Method, to determine the number of lashings required.

- Lashings should be fitted where appropriate to the chassis, axles, towing points or any lashing points which are fitted. Lashings must not cause damage to the fitting being used. These lashings should be lead variously forward, aft and to port and to starboard.

- Lashings are most effective when they make an angle with the deck of between 30º and 60º. Lashings should not be crossed from side to side; they should be lead outboard and down in a well balanced arrangement.

- The parking brakes should be applied and locked if fitted, and machines with diesel engines should not be left in gear during the voyage.

- As with road vehicles carried on board, lashings should be examined at frequent and regular intervals and all lashings found to be slack should be re-tightened. If thought appropriate, because of movement of the vehicles or adverse weather predicted for later in the voyage, additional lashings should be fitted as appropriate.

Tracked Vehicles and Machinery
Such machines are carried on ro-ro vessels and conventional vessels. They are, mostly, heavy items and should be treated as such. Things to remember are as follows:

- Details of the dimensions, location of centre of gravity, etc. should be obtained from the shippers.

- Calculations to determine the required number of lashings should be carried out using the Advanced Calculation Method. If shippers cannot provide all the necessary information then calculations using the Rule-of-Thumb method should be carried out.

- Calculations to determine the area over which the weight of the machine should be spread over the hatch cover, deck or tank-top to be used must be completed.

- Good quality timber dunnage should be provided and laid out in way of where the vehicles or machines are to be carried.

- Lashings should be fitted to strong points on the items and should be lead variously forward, aft and to both sides, such that the strength of the lashing system complies with the requirements of the Advanced Calculation Method or the Rule-of-Thumb method. Lashings must not cause damage to the fitting being used.

- The positioning of the items, one adjacent to the next, and the arrangements of lashings, should satisfy good seamanship practice, such that there is sufficient room between adjacent items and between lashings so that ship's staff can carry out routine examinations and tighten lashings which are found to be slack. If movement of the items is found, or if adverse weather is predicted for later in the voyage, additional lashings should be fitted as appropriate.

TIMBER CARGOES - ON AND UNDER DECK

Timber cargo being loaded on deck.

The Code of Safe Practice for Ships Carrying Timber Deck Cargoes, is published by the IMO. This Code will be referred to throughout this section. Additionally, maritime nations issue their own regulations, recommendations and requirements with regard to the loading and stowage of timber cargo at their own ports. For example, Canada Transport issue the Canadian Timber Regulations which must be followed when loading at Canadian ports. Before loading a timber cargo, be it of logs, cants, packaged timber, or a combination of these, the IMO Code and the national requirements must be studied and all of the requirements and recommendations must be complied with and/or followed. The provisions of the IMO Code will be described but requirements, etc., published by maritime nations will not be dealt with here.

The Code and its Appendices give recommendations on the various aspects of timber cargoes, including the following:

- The general preparation of the vessel before loading timber on deck.
- The height and extent of the deck cargo, depending upon the load line assigned to the vessel.
- Specifications for the strength of lashings, the minimum tension in those lashings when used to secure the cargo, the spacing between the lashings and means to adjust them during the voyage.
- Specification and spacing of uprights.
- Guidance on the stowage and securing of different types of timber cargoes.
- Matters relating to personnel protection and safety devices, including means of access to and from the deck.

- Action to be taken during the voyage, both if no incident occurs and if things go wrong and there is a shift of cargo for whatever reason.

- Stability of the vessel throughout of the voyage.

- As Appendix B, general guidelines for the under deck stowage of logs.

Throughout the previous sections of this guide recommendations have been given with regard to the ways in which items of cargo can be secured such that they will not shift unless there are exceptional circumstances. In other words, the philosophy has been - *secure the item such that it should not shift.*

The philosophy behind the stowage and securing of a timber deck cargo is somewhat different and may be summarised as:

The stowage is satisfactorily secured for normally expected circumstances but lashings are not so strong as to retain the cargo on board if it shifts, and those lashings are fitted with quick release devices for use in an emergency situation.

When compared with the Rule-of-Thumb method for calculating the number of lashings, the Timber Deck Cargoes Code requires a very small number of lashings for the weight of a full deck cargo of timber. To ensure that a timber deck cargo is carried safely, therefore, all of the provisions of the Code which apply to the carrying vessel and the particular type of cargo must be followed, completely. Departure from the requirements and recommendations might lead to a shift of cargo and the development of a very dangerous situation.

There are a number of fundamental issues which must be borne in mind when planning the loading and stowage of timber on deck. These are as follows:

- The type of vessel and whether or not she has been assigned a timber load line.

- The type of timber to be carried.

- The height and the forward and aft extent of the stowage.

- The type of lashings required and their spacing along the deck, and whether or not uprights are to be used.

- The stability of the vessel throughout the voyage.

- The stowage of the cargo must be such that the cargo, the securing arrangements and ship's fittings are variously accessible by the crew, closed beforehand and/or kept clear. Also, visibility from the navigation bridge must be acceptable.

- Cargo jettisoning arrangements.

These various points must be considered together, not in isolation. A shipment of timber cannot be accepted for loading on the basis that the height to which it will be stowed will not interfere with the navigation of the vessel only to find at a later time that the maximum permissible deck loading has been exceeded, and the vessel has a negative GM.

TYPE OF VESSEL

It is believed that a complete stowage of tightly stowed timber will increase the vessel's reserve of buoyancy. This being the case, a vessel with such a stowage of timber may be safely loaded to a deeper draft than would normally be allowed. Turning that around, a vessel which is fitted and capable of carrying a full deck cargo of timber may be assigned a timber load line. When a timber deck cargo is to be loaded such that the vessel will make use of her timber load line the stowage must extend, as given in paragraph 3.2.3 of the Code, over the full length of the well or wells between superstructures and athwartship as close as possible to the ship's sides. The cargo stowed in the holds has no bearing upon whether or not the timber load line may be used. The use of the timber load line is only dependent upon the stowage of a timber deck cargo.

If the vessel does not have a timber load line then clearly she cannot load deeper than the appropriate load line for the load port and the voyage.

TYPES OF TIMBER

Timber carried by ocean vessels is categorised into two types, loose or packaged sawn timber, and logs, poles, cants or similar cargo.

These two categories of timber require different lashing arrangements because they are stowed in different ways and the resultant stowages are somewhat different.

Loose and packaged sawn timber is stowed in regular tiers across the vessel with outboard packs in the athwartships line and inboard packs variously longitudinal or athwartships as appropriate. Some of the packs might be ragged at one end and large gaps might exist around deckhouses, masts, etc. Additionally, owing to the dimensions of the packs, it is unlikely that they will be capable of being stowed compactly between and up against uprights to port and to starboard. This being the case, it is likely that there will be a large amount of vacant space within a stowage of packaged sawn timber and this in turn means there is a possibility of shifting of packs into adjacent vacant spaces.

Logs, poles, etc. can be stowed compactly together, upper items stowing neatly in the cantlins, so to speak, of lower items, and densely between the uprights to port and to starboard such that there is a minimum of vacant space into which any of the logs or poles can shift. However, a stowage of logs will settle as individual logs move slightly when the vessel rolls and pitches during the voyage.

Cants are defined as being logs which are slab-cut, ripped lengthwise so that the resulting thick piece of timber has two opposing, parallel flat sides and in some cases a third side which is sawn flat. Cants might be shipped loose or in packages. The packages might retain their integrity but might be only loosely bounded and therefore might have a tendency to assume a rounded cross-section within the bands. Under the circumstances, cants might sometimes be considered to be loose or packaged sawn timber, but might otherwise be categorised together with logs. If in doubt seek advice.

HEIGHT AND FORWARD AND AFT EXTENT OF STOWAGE

The only specific height restriction is that given for a vessel operating within a seasonal winter zone in winter, when the height should not exceed ⅓ of the extreme breadth of the ship. Otherwise, the height of a timber deck cargo should be restricted so that:

- Adequate forward visibility is assured.

- A safe margin of stability is maintained at all stages of the voyage.

- Any forward-facing profiles do not present overhanging shoulders to a head sea.

- The weight of the timber deck cargo does not exceed the designated maximum permissible load of the weather deck and hatches.

There are, however, other factors which may affect the height to which timber can be stowed on deck. The vessel might have substantial fashion plates to port and to starboard at the forward shoulders and therefore there may be no overhanging shoulders to the stowage. A timber deck cargo should not be stowed above the height of derricks or crane jibs when these are stowed. Also, the stowage should not be to a height at the sides greater than the height of the uprights. If the vessel is designed for the carriage of timber deck cargo there is probably on board a timber deck stowage plan which gives details of lashing arrangements and the height to which timber may be stowed. There will also be guidance in the Cargo Securing Manual.

With regard to the forward and aft extent of the cargo the only restrictions are with regard to stowage on board a vessel when the timber load line is being used. The code requires that the timber should be stowed so as to extend over the entire available length of the deck and outboard as close as possible to the ship's side, as given in paragraph 3.2.3 of the Code. When a timber cargo is being stowed on the deck of a vessel without a timber load line that cargo should be stowed compactly and, so far as possible, over the entire available space on deck in order that lashing arrangements in accordance with the Code can be set up.

LASHINGS AND UPRIGHTS

Lashings
Lashings can be of chain or wire, with other components such as shackles, rigging screws, snatch blocks, slip hooks, etc. These components must have a breaking strength of not less than 133 kN (13.3 tonnes). The lashings should pass over the timber deck cargo and be shackled to eye plates or other strong points of adequate strength, that is more than 133 kN. Each lashing should be provided with a tightening device so that the lashing can be tightened initially and can be tightened as required during the voyage. All such equipment should be in good condition with all threads and other moving parts well greased. All lashings are to be fitted with quick release mechanisms, either slip hooks, in the case of chain lashings, or wiggle wires in the case of wire lashings. These systems are all described in the Code of Safe Practice for Ships Carrying Timber Deck Cargoes

All timber deck cargoes should be secured throughout their length by independent lashings. The lashing requirements for loose or packaged sawn timber are different from those for logs, poles, cants or similar cargo. The requirement for loose or packaged sawn timber are as follows:

- The maximum spacing of lashings should be 3 m for stowage height up to 4 m and 1.5 m for heights of more than 4 m.

- Packages stowed at the upper outboard edge of the stow should be secured by at least two lashings each.

- If the timber items are of length less than 3.6 m the spacing of the lashing should be reduced as necessary.

- Rounded angle pieces of suitable material and design should be used along the upper outboard edge of the stow to bear the stress and permit free reeving of the lashing.

The requirements for logs, poles, cants or similar cargo are as follows:

- The maximum spacing of the independent lashings should be not more than 3 m, irrespective of the height of the stowage.

- Uprights should be rigged and athwartships lashings (hog lashings) joining each port and starboard pair of uprights should be rigged; one near the top of the stow and others at other levels appropriate to the height of the stow.

- A lashing system to tighten the stow comprising a combination of wiggle wires and foot wires should be fitted. Foot wires should be set up leading from padeyes on deck up to the top of the stowage, terminating in a snatch block, and the wiggle wire should be passed from side to side over the top of the stowage zig-zagging between the foot wire snatch blocks, being made fast at one end and being led to a winch or other tensioning device at the other.

- If appropriate for cants, rounded angle pieces of suitable material and design should be used along the upper outboard edge of the stow to bear the stress and permit free reeving of the lashings.

Uprights
We now come to the question of uprights. Uprights are required when a cargo of logs, poles, etc. is to be carried, because there is a requirement for hog lashings between the pairs of uprights, whereas there is no requirement for hog lashings between uprights, and therefore no absolute requirement for uprights, when a cargo of loose or packaged sawn timber is carried. However, uprights should be fitted when required by the nature, height or character of the timber deck cargo. It is clear, therefore, that if logs are to be carried uprights must be rigged and hog lashings fitted.

With regard to loose and packaged timber, if the vessel is fitted with collapsible steel uprights which can be easily rigged, these should be rigged for the intended voyage. If the vessel has on board timber uprights and these can be rigged, they should be rigged. If the vessel is not fitted with any form of upright then it is not essential to arrange for uprights to be provided and fitted. If uprights are fitted for a stowage of lose or packaged sawn timber it is recommended here that, unless there is an overriding reason for the fitting of hog wires, hog wires should not be fitted, this is because on the one hand they provide no benefit in the way that they do for a cargo of logs by producing an inboard pull on the respective uprights, whereas on the other hand they might restrict a jettisoning operation by holding back on board packs which have shifted only a small amount; the jettisoning of logs would not be so restricted by hog wires.

STABILITY DURING THE VOYAGE

The requirements for stability are set out in the Code and must be followed. From paragraph 2.5 and Appendix C of the Code:

The GMo (initial metacentric height) should preferably not exceed 3% of the breadth of the vessel and should not be less than 0.15m, or 0.10m if certain additional provisions are met, at all times during the voyage whilst other criteria should be complied with.

It is essential that the vessel must have an acceptable measure of stability whilst not being too stiff. If the vessel has a large GM her role period will be short, and heavy rolling in a short period might put excessive loading on the securing arrangements. A balance must be achieved between the weight of the deck cargo and the amount of ballast water taken to give the vessel the required amount of stability.

STOWAGE

The loading and stowage of a deck cargo of timber must be carried out and completed in such a way that all hatches, doors, etc. which must be closed for the voyage are closed before they are over-stowed and such that any parts of the stowage or the vessel which must be accessible by the crew during the voyage remain or are made accessible before departure.

It must also be remembered that the stowage must not interfere with visibility from the bridge and the navigation of the vessel.

CARGO JETTISONING ARRANGEMENTS

When loading timber on deck lashings most incorporate slip hooks or other devices which allow quick release of the lashings if necessary during the voyage. The devices must be examined before being brought into use to confirm that they are in good and well lubricated condition, suitable for the intended voyage and not in any way deflective. During the voyage the devices must be maintained in good working condition.

If the cargo shifts and it becomes necessary for all, or part of the cargo to be jettisoned, release of lashings might be necessary. If circumstances mean that access to the slip hooks, or other devices, is impossible or dangerous, or if the slip hooks become strained and inoperative, it might be necessary to use other means to let the lashings go. Consideration should be given, at the commencement of the voyage, depending upon the size of the lashings in use, to the use of cutting devices including axes, wire or bolt cutters and electrical cutting equipment. Consideration should be given to what equipment might be needed if jettisoning becomes necessary, and such equipment should be kept in a suitable place ready for use.

PRECAUTIONS DURING THE VOYAGE

During the voyage it will be necessary for members of the crew to proceed on deck and onto the stowage of timber in order to check the lashings and tighten them where necessary and to make other inspections. Some points to remember are as follows:

- Members of the crew should wear suitable protective clothing when working on deck.

- Equipment used by the crew should be suitable for the intended task and in good, serviceable condition.

- If there is no convenient passage on or below the deck guide lines or rails, and where appropriate an even walking surface, should be provided on each side of the deck cargo. Additionally a lifeline should be fitted at the centre line of the vessel. Ladders, steps or ramps should be fitted to provide access from the deck to the top of the stowage.

- Lashings should be carefully examined and tightened at the beginning of the voyage. Lashings should be examined and tightened as appropriate at regular intervals throughout the voyage. Entries should be made in the log book, recording details of inspections.

- The voyage should be planned so as to avoid areas where severe sea conditions are predicted. Weather reports, weather facsimile or weather routeing agencies should be consulted in order to achieve this.

- If severe weather or sea conditions are encountered a reduction in the vessel's speed and/or an alternation in the course in order to minimise the motion of the vessel and the forces imposed on the cargo, structures and lashings should be considered. The lashings are not designed to provide a means of securing against imprudent ship handling in heavy weather. There is no substitute for good seamanship.

- If there is a major shift of deck cargo which causes the vessel to list, examinations should be carried out to determine the precise cause or causes of the list and then appropriate action should be taken.

- If timber deck cargo is jettisoned or is accidentally lost overboard, the master must advise the authorities of the closest country, he should also notify owners of the vessel and any charterers.

TIMBER STOWED UNDER-DECK

Logs stowed under-deck.

Appendix B of the Code gives some general guidelines for the under-deck stowage of logs. The guidelines give recommended safe practices to be carried out prior to loading, during loading operations and during the voyage. Logs can range in size from small poles to large hardwood logs of weight in excess of 20 tonnes. Logs are sometimes relatively dry and others are saturated being lifted from rafts brought alongside. The loading and stowage of logs present particular problems which must be addressed.

Logs are heavy and are awkward to handle and stow. Water may run off or out of the logs and that water must be pumped overboard. Because the logs are wet, to a greater or lesser degree, microbiological organisms (moulds, etc.,) will grow on and in the timber, and the respiration of those organisms will use oxygen which, in turn, will lead to oxygen depletion of the atmosphere within the cargo compartment.

These recommendations are specifically for the stowage of logs but most apply just as much to other timber cargoes such as lose or packaged sawn timber, cants, poles and any other products. In brief, points to be remembered are as follows:

- The cargo compartment should be clean and dry before loading and the bilges should be clean and dry, and tested for satisfactory operation, before commencement of loading.
- All lifting equipment should be examined prior to use and determined to be in satisfactory condition. Any defects should be rectified before commencement of cargo operations.
- Lifts should be brought on board carefully without excessive swinging in order to avoid the possibility of damage to ship's fittings or injury to personnel.
- Stowage should be tight and compact without avoidable gaps and areas of vacant space.
- Items should be stowed in the fore-and-aft line of the vessel so far as possible with items aligned athwartships to fill gaps and vacant space within and around the stowage.

Before any members of the crew enter the cargo compartment during the voyage that compartment should be thoroughly ventilated and the atmosphere within the compartment should be tested at different levels for oxygen deficiency and harmful vapours. If there is any doubt as to the nature of the atmosphere self-contained breathing apparatus should be worn by all persons entering the compartment.

As a final word, it is stressed that the provisions of the Code of Safe Practice for Ships Carrying Timber Deck Cargo, should be followed whenever a timber deck cargo, of whatever type, is carried.

CONTAINERS - ON AND UNDER DECK - CONTAINER AND NON-CONTAINER VESSELS

Containers loaded on deck.

Containers can be successfully carried on board vessels designed and fitted for their carriage and on board other vessels provided there are suitable lashings and fittings for the safe stowage and securing of the containers. Containers are, mostly, of length either 20 ft or 40 ft and of height ranging from 8 ft to 9 ft 6 in, but all are of a standard width of 8 ft. Containers are of a variety of types including general cargo units, refrigerated units, flat racks, tanktainers, etc. These various types of unit carry different commodities from cartons of goods, machinery, refrigerated produce or pharmaceuticals, through to all types of liquid.

Containers are not solid boxes of huge strength which can be stowed on board with little care or concern for either the container or its contents; they are, in fact, of fragile construction except for their corner posts and base support structure, and they must be stowed, secured and cared for properly and appropriately bearing in mind the type of vessel upon which they are carried and the cargo stowed inside.

STRENGTH OF CONTAINERS

Only the end framework, and particularly the end corner posts, and the base frame are designed to take loadings. All other parts of the container are non-strength members and are there only for the protection and preservation of the cargo carried. The base framework is designed to have sufficient strength to carry the cargo. The four corner posts are designed to take the load of any containers stowed on top and to withstand forces encountered during lifting, variously during loading and discharging operations and during handling ashore. Additionally, the container might be fitted for handling by a fork lift truck. Cross members within the end frames are designed to withstand racking forces. Containers must therefore be stowed bearing the following points in mind:

- The container must be stowed on all four bottom corner castings only, either on the ground or on board.

- One container must be stowed squarely atop another such that all four corner posts are vertically in line.

- Break bulk cargo must not be stowed on top of containers.

- Break bulk cargo must not be stowed against, secured to or shored against the sides or ends of a container.

If these general rules are not followed damage will be sustained by the container. If it is not suitably supported on its four corner castings but is partly supported by the stiffening members below the floor, those floor stiffeners will buckle and the container will become racked. If break bulk cargo is stowed atop or beside, or is secured to the container, the top panel, the sides or ends will be deformed because they are not designed to withstand large loadings; they are simply there to keep the rain out.

Also, because a container is designed to have strength only in its end frameworks and floor, they must be secured in an approved manner. Securing of containers is discussed below.

STOWAGE OF GOODS IN AND ON CONTAINERS

The cargo carried in or on a container must be properly stowed and adequately secured such that it will not move during the voyage. Cargo on flat or other open units can be examined prior to loading and the suitability of the stowage and securing arrangements can be determined. If those arrangements are not satisfactory the unit should be refused shipment. The doors of a closed unit are usually sealed and therefore the cargo within cannot be inspected. However, if there is any doubt with regard to the cargo inside a container, the appropriate personnel should be contacted and the containers should be opened for inspection and for any remedial work to be completed.

The packing of containers should be done in a logical and balanced sequence. The side panels, the end panel and the doors have limited strength and the floor has, as the deck of a ship has, a maximum permissible loading, and these factors should be borne in mind. Some basic rules are as follows:

- The weight of the cargo should be spread over the whole of the floor or, in the case of heavy items, over a sufficient area to support the weight of the item.

- The weight of the cargo should be distributed evenly over the breadth and length of the container such that the overall centre of gravity is as close as possible to being above the centre of the floor.

- Heavy items should be secured in the container by timber chocking and bracing to the floor, to both sides and to both ends of the unit.

- Where different types of cargo are to be stowed together (any combination of drums, cartons, cases, bags, etc.,) heavy items must be stowed below lighter items, wet items must be stowed below dry items and non-compatible items should never be stowed together.

- Where two or more tiers of items such as drums are to be stowed in a container, consideration should be given to the fitting of timber, plywood or other sheet separations between tiers in order to stabilize the stowage.

- Items should be stowed, so far as possible, from side to side and end to end within the unit and compactly tight against each other. If this is not possible the sides and ends of the units should be adequately chocked or braced, or chocking within the stowage should be completed by the use of appropriate dunnaging; air bags, timber, plywood, matting, etc.

CONTAINER VESSELS

Container vessels are fitted with a system for the stowage and securing of the containers, both on-deck and under-deck, which has been approved by a Classification Society. That stowage and securing system will therefore have been constructed such that the containers will be satisfactorily held in position throughout the voyage provided that the stowage and securing system has been used in accordance with the requirements laid down by the manufacturer, and as set out the vessel's Cargo Securing Manual, and provided that the voyage is completed with the observance of good seamanship and navigation practice. No system can, of course, guard against exceptional circumstances being encountered during the voyage.

Container securing systems comprise, broadly speaking, either cell guides or a combination of fittings. Containers loaded in cell guides do not need to be separately secured because the cell guides will fully retain the containers. Securing systems comprising various fittings have been designed for both on-deck and under-deck stowages. The vessel's Cargo Securing Manual will contain details of all pieces of equipment and where they are to be used. Fittings will include items such as stacking cones, bridge fittings, tension-pressure elements, twist-locks, lashing bars and turnbuckles. The vessel might be provided with a system similar to that designed by MacGregor-Conver GmbH below.

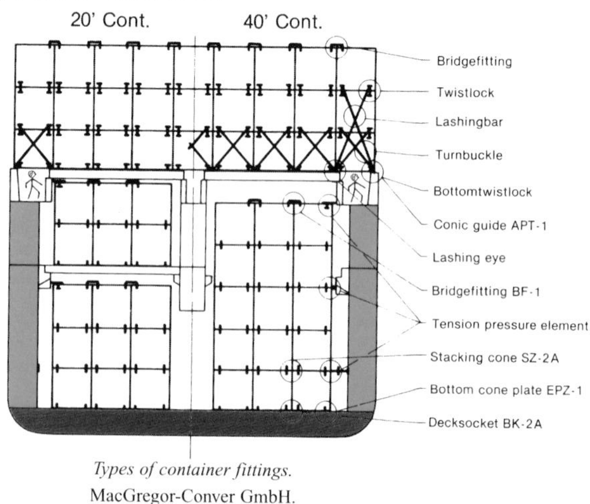

Types of container fittings.
MacGregor-Conver GmbH.

Points to be remembered when using container securing fittings are as follows:

- All securing devices must be applied as shown in the Cargo Securing Manual.

- All securing devices in use must be in good condition with all moving parts free and well greased.

- Defective securing devices should be removed from use and placed in a suitable receptacle so that they can be landed for repair or destruction.

- Routine inspections of the equipment should be carried out and records of such inspections kept. Any maintenance work which can be carried out should be completed and details recorded in the appropriate records attached to the Cargo Securing Manual.

- Any equipment found on board which is not from the vessel's outfit should be landed at an appropriate port.

- Twist-locks can be either left-locking or right-locking. The ship's outfit should include only one type of twist-lock. Any twist-locks which lock the wrong way should be immediately set to one side and not used, and should be landed at an appropriate port.

The container securing system will have been designed on the basis of certain arrangements of containers, that is, with regard to the overall weight of a stack of containers and such that heavier containers are lower down in stowage and lighter containers are further up. When planning the stowage of containers the following points should be borne in mind.

- The total weight of each stack of containers should not exceed the permissible stack this having been determined for the tank-top, deck or hatch cover.

- Tier weight distributions given in the Cargo Securing Manual should not be exceeded.

Flats and open top containers are often used to carry items such as large pieces of machinery or large cases which extend beyond the top or sides of the unit. Such over-height or over-wide units will need additional space and this must be borne in mind when planning the stowage of such special containers.

Containers with refrigerated goods will also need appropriate stowage such that their refrigeration machinery can be connected to the vessel's electricity supply. Another group of specials are containers carrying hazardous goods. The requirements of the IMDG Code must be complied with. There are sections within the IMDG Code which give guidance with regard to the stowage of containers and the necessary separation between different types of hazardous materials.

NON-CONTAINER VESSELS

Containers can be carried by vessels which are not container vessels, but special attention should be given to the stowage and securing of the containers. Non-container vessels can be divided into two types, those which are fitted with container securing devices and those which have none. The securing devices on board might range from the fittings shown in illustration 6, through to just bottom stacking devices on deck and securing chains. If the vessel is provided with a full outfit, although she is not classed as a container vessel, the recommendations given above for container vessels should be followed.

The Code of Safe Practice for Cargo Stowage and Securing gives some guidance for the stowage and securing of containers on the decks of vessels which are not specifically designed and fitted for containers. The illustrations given in the Code show containers stowed 2 high. The United Kingdom Department of Trade Merchant Shipping Notice no.624 - October 1971 stated that:

Except where there is provision enabling a twist-lock, or other similar device, to be inserted in the bottom corner fittings of the container and into suitably designed recesses in the hatch covers or fabricated deck stools of appropriate strength, containers carried on-deck should be stowed one high only.

It is recommended here that if the vessel is fitted with deck or hatch top stools or seating devices containers may be stowed two high, whereas if there are no such fittings containers should be stowed one high only.

When stowing and securing containers on vessels fitted with deck or hatch top stools or seating devices the following points should be borne in mind.

- Containers should be stowed in the fore-and-aft direction and squarely supported on all four bottom corner castings.
- Containers should be stowed and secured such that there is sufficient space around each container, or stack of two containers, to allow personnel access to all securing arrangements during the voyage.
- The weight of the containers should not overstress the deck or hatch top.
- Container fittings such as twist-locks, bridge fittings, lashing chains and turnbuckles should be in good condition and working order, adequately greased where appropriate.
- All securing devices should be used in accordance with the information given in the vessel's Cargo Securing Manual.
- If wire rope is used to secure the containers such wire should be of adequate strength, should be in good condition and eyes or grommets should be made up with the appropriate number of wire rope grips in the correct arrangement.
- On board a vessel fitted with deck stools and hatch-top fittings, the containers may be stowed two high and must be secured by the use of twist-locks, chain or wire rope lashings, turnbuckles and other fittings such as bridge fittings, timber shores and chocks.

When containers are to be stowed directly onto the deck or hatch-top the following additional points should be borne in mind:

- Containers should be stowed only one high.
- The corner castings should be stowed on timber gratings or timber boards of sufficient thickness and rigidity such that the weight of the container is spread over a sufficient area of the deck or hatch top so as the maximum permissible loading is not exceeded.
- No dunnage should be placed such that it is in contact with the underneath of the floor structure, sills or side frames.
- Containers must be stowed and secured independently.
- Lashings must be of adequate strength for the weight of the container and lashings should be led from top corner castings to deck fitting of appropriate strength either crossed from side to side or leading down and outboard/inboard from the top corner castings. The requirement for the strength of the lashings should be calculated using the Rule-of-Thumb method or the Advanced Calculation Method, depending upon the amount of information available.
- Foot lashings or foot chocks should be fitted in way of bottom corner castings. Foot lashings of either wire or chain should be lead from bottom corner castings directly

outboard/inboard to deck lashing points. Alternatively, foot chocks constructed from good quality timber should be fitted between bottom corner castings and the hatch coaming structure inboard and bulwark structure outboard. Such foot chocks should be of length no more than 2m.

- All lashings should be set tight by turnbuckles.

If the container is not adequately secured it is likely to move and if the cargo in the container is not secured in the container that cargo is likely to move as well.

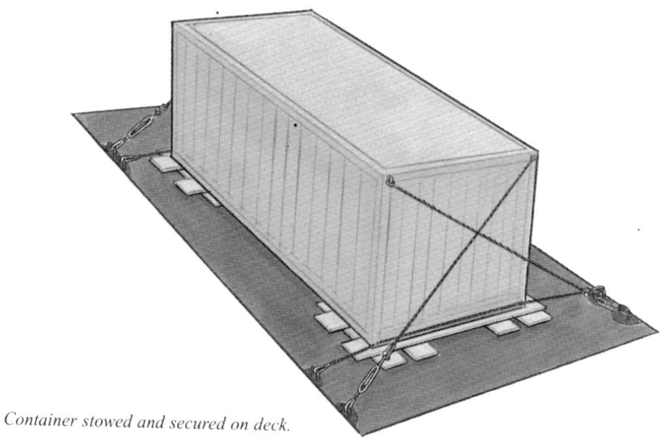

Container stowed and secured on deck.

Damaged container.

SECTION THREE - THE VOYAGE

Setting off on the voyage.

Any voyage can be divided into three main sections, so far as the planning of things and the checking for departures from those plans is concerned.

These sections are; loading and securing, passage planning and actions during the voyage. The three are, of course, inter-linked and each depends on the other two.

LOADING AND SECURING

The loading and securing of items of cargo must be carefully planned before operations begin and carried out in accordance with that plan, although some necessary adjustments to the plan might become apparent during the operations. The basic rules to be borne in mind are as follows:

- The cargo compartment should be clean and dry, and in every way prepared and suitable for the intended cargo.
- Detailed information about the cargo should be obtained, including: the types of cargo to be loaded; the weight of cargo items; the dimensions, centre of gravity, etc. of individual pieces; the position and strength of lashing points and lifting points and any other information which is appropriate to the particular cargo.
- The stowage of cargo should be planned in detail bearing in mind load port rotation, discharge port rotation, cargo stowage requirements, cargo securing requirements and access to items of cargo during the voyage.
- Strength and stability calculations should be completed to confirm that the stowage plan is satisfactory. If it is found that the vessel's stability or strength requirements are not met changes to the stowage plan should be made.
- The stowage and securing of the cargo should be carried out in accordance with the plan and in accordance with the vessel's Cargo Securing Manual.

- The stowage and securing of cargo should be completed before the vessel leaves the loading port.

PASSAGE PLANNING

Passage planning is the term used for the planning of the route from the load port to the discharge port and the setting of courses and laying them on the appropriate charts. Passage planning also involves the consideration of weather and sea conditions likely to be encountered during the voyage because those conditions will affect the cargo. For example the master of a ro-ro ferry employed on a service across the Irish Sea will instruct his crew to fit more lashings to the vehicles during winter months, when gales are forecast, than he will during summer months when there is an anticyclone stationary and centred over Ireland, such that only light winds are forecast. Passage planning and the planning of loading and securing are, clearly, closely linked and must be carried out in conjunction, one with the other. Points to be borne in mind are as follows:

- Passage planning must include the determination of what weather and sea conditions are likely to be encountered at all stages of the voyage. If adverse weather is likely to be encountered during any stage of the voyage the stowage and securing arrangements can be adjusted in order to take into account the probability that the vessel will roll and pitch heavily during the voyage.

- If it is believed that the cargo or the lashing arrangements cannot withstand heavy rolling and pitching of the vessel, such as might be the case with project cargo, one option might be to adjust the passage plan in order to ensure that the vessel does not encounter adverse weather.

ACTIONS DURING THE VOYAGE

During the voyage, be it a short coastal passage of only a few hours or a long ocean voyage between continents, the master and his crew should carry out certain actions to ensure that the cargo is carried carefully and safely without endangering the cargo itself, the carrying vessel or the crew. The progress of the vessel and the condition should be monitored and the cargo and the securing devices must be inspected and adjusted when and where necessary. If adverse weather or sea conditions are encountered actions should be taken to minimise the motions of the vessel in order to minimise the accelerations acting upon the cargo, and thereby keep to a minimum the loadings on the securing arrangements. Things to be borne in mind are as follows:

- Weather forecasts should be obtained for at least the next 24 hours before departure from the load port and throughout the voyage until arrival at the discharge port. Those weather forecasts should be studied in order to determine what weather and sea conditions are likely to be encountered. Such weather monitoring should be a continuous process.

- If adverse weather and sea conditions are forecast then actions might be necessary. Such actions might include increasing the number of lashings fitted to items of cargo, ballasting or de-ballasting to improve the behaviour of the vessel or an alternation of course and/or speed to minimise the vessel's motions or to avoid the area of adverse conditions altogether.

- If adverse weather and sea conditions develop without much warning it might be necessary to take urgent action to increase the securing arrangement and an alternation of course and/or speed might be appropriate in the short term, or it might be necessary to heave the vessel to in order to ease her motion. Ballasting or de-ballasting might also improve the vessel's behaviour but account must always be taken of the vessel's stability because such ballasting or de-ballasting must not give the vessel excessive or insufficient stability.

- The cargo and the securing arrangements should be monitored throughout the voyage and the securing arrangements should be adjusted as and when necessary. It is normal practice to complete an inspection of the cargo compartments and deck daily during good weather conditions and twice or three times daily, as found necessary and appropriate during adverse weather conditions.

- If cargo shifts during the voyage the vessel's course and/or speed should be reduced to ease the vessel's motion, or she should be hove-to, in order that re-stowing and re-securing of the cargo, where possible, can be completed.

- If cargo has shifted and lashings have failed to an extent that the crew cannot re-stow and re-secure the cargo while the vessel is at sea, a deviation of course to a place of shelter should be completed. If appropriate, the vessel should be taken to a port of refuge where re-stowage and re-securing can be carried out properly.

- The integrity of the vessel should be monitored throughout the voyage to ensure that damage has not been sustained by shifting cargo or by lashings, or by any other cause.

Cargo spaces, like any other enclosed spaces might suffer from oxygen depletion. Cargo compartments should be thoroughly ventilated and the atmosphere should be tested before members of the crew enter. All checks and recommendations with regard to the entry of enclosed spaces should be completed on every occasion.

APPENDICES

APPENDIX A - SOLAS CHAPTER VI, PART A, REGULATION 5

Stowage and securing

1. Cargo and cargo units carried on or under deck shall be so loaded, stowed and secured as to prevent as far as is practicable, throughout the voyage, damage or hazard to the ship and the persons on board, and loss of cargo overboard.

2. Cargo carried in a cargo unit shall be so packed and secured within the unit as to prevent, throughout the voyage, damage or hazard to the ship and the persons on board.

3. Appropriate precautions shall be taken during loading and transport of heavy cargoes or cargoes with abnormal physical dimensions to ensure that no structural damage to the ship occurs and to maintain adequate stability throughout the voyage.

4. Appropriate precautions shall be taken during loading and transport of cargo units on board ro-ro ships, especially with regard to the securing arrangements on board such ships and on the cargo units and with regard to the strength of the securing points and lashings.

5. Containers shall not be loaded to more than the maximum gross weight indicated on the Safety Approval Plate under the International Convention for Safe Containers (CSC).

6. Cargo units, including containers, shall be loaded, stowed and secured throughout the voyage in accordance with the Cargo Securing Manual approved by the Administration . In ships with ro-ro cargo spaces, as defined in regulation II-2/3.14, all securing of cargo units, in accordance with the Cargo Securing Manual, shall be completed before the ship leaves the berth. The Cargo Securing Manual shall be drawn up to a standard at least equivalent to the guidelines developed by the Organisation.

APPENDIX B - GUIDELINES FOR THE PREPARATION OF THE CARGO SECURING MANUAL, PREAMBLE

Regulations VI/5 and VII/6 of the 1974 SOLAS Convention require cargo units and cargo transport units to be loaded, stowed and secured throughout the voyage in accordance with a Cargo Securing Manual approved by the Administration and drawn up to a standard at least equivalent to the guidelines developed by the Organisation.

IMO's Maritime Safety Committee (MSC), at its sixty-sixth session (28 May to 6 June 1996), considered draft guidelines for the preparation of the Cargo Securing Manual prepared by the Sub-Committee on Dangerous Goods, Solid Cargoes and Containers at its first session (5 to 9 February 1996), and approved the Guidelines presented in this publication, which were originally issued as MSC/Circ.745 (dated 13 June 1996).

These Guidelines are based on the provisions contained in the annex to MSC/Circ.385 (dated 8 January 1985) but have been expanded to include the applications explicit to ships which are equipped or adapted for the carriage of freight containers, taking into account the provisions of the Code of Safe Practice for Cargo Stowage and Securing (CSS Code), as amended. They are of a general nature and intended to provide guidance on the preparation of Cargo Securing Manuals, which are required on all types of ships engaged in the carriage of cargoes other than solid and liquid bulk cargoes.

Member Governments are invited to bring these Guidelines to the attention of all parties concerned, with the aim of having Cargo Securing Manuals carried on board ships prepared appropriately and in a consistent manner, and to implement them as soon as possible and, in any case, not later than 31 December 1997. The Guidelines supersede those presented in MSC/Circ.385.

APPENDIX C - ADVANCED CALCULATION METHOD

The Advanced Calculation Method assesses the balance between forces and moments in terms of three motions, as follows:-

- Transverse sliding forces to port and to starboard.
- Transverse tipping moments to port and to starboard.
- Longitudinal sliding forces in the fore-and-aft direction both forward and aft.

As mentioned earlier, the motions of a ship are longitudinal (fore-and-aft), transverse (athwartships) and vertical. In addition, a piece of cargo carried on deck will experience forces produced by wind pressure and by sea sloshing when waves are shipped on deck.

The basic formula for the calculation of the external forces (**Step Two**) is given as follows:-

$$F_{(x,y,z)} = m. a_{(x,y,z)} + Fw_{(x,y)} + Fs_{(x,y)}$$

Where F is the longitudinal ($_x$), transverse ($_y$), and vertical ($_z$), force as appropriate, and:-

m	=	Mass of the unit in tonnes.
a	=	Longitudinal ($_x$), transverse ($_y$), and vertical ($_z$), accelerations (from tables).
Fw	=	Longitudinal ($_x$), and transverse ($_y$), forces produced by wind pressure.
Fs	=	Longitudinal ($_x$), and transverse ($_y$), forces produced by sea sloshing.

A worked example of an Advanced Calculation Method is described in **Appendix D** with the calculation set out on the form developed for this guide attached; a blank version of the form is in **Appendix E**. Follow the steps of the calculation while reading the description below.

STEP ONE - INPUTS AND PRIMARY CALCULATIONS

The mass of the unit will of course be known, in tonnes. This should be listed together with its dimensions in metres (width, length and height), its lever arms of stableness and tipping in the athwartships line and its position on board. It would be good practice to also list, for easy reference, the vessel's length, breadth, GM and speed.

Having set out all the basic input information the primary calculations or assessments can be carried out to determine the accelerations and the wind and sea forces needed for **Step Two**.

The longitudinal, transverse and vertical accelerations (a_x, a_y and a_z) are obtained from Table 2 - Basic acceleration data, of Annex 13, that table is based upon the vessel being of length 100 m and having a speed of 15 knots, and being on an ocean voyage at any time of the year, where the voyage is of 25 days duration. The transverse acceleration is of course dependent upon the height and fore-and-aft location of the stowage position, the longitudinal acceleration is dependent only upon the height and the vertical acceleration is dependent only upon the fore-and-aft position of the unit. Table 2 must, therefore, be entered on the basis of the stowage position in terms of height and fore-and-aft location.

For vessels of length other than 100 m and of a speed other than 15 knots a single correction must be applied to each of the three basic acceleration factors, and that correction can be obtained from Table 3.

The basic formula is also based upon the roll period of the vessel being satisfactorily long for the size of the vessel. As will be recalled, the roll period of the vessel affects the transverse acceleration, and therefore the transverse forces, acting on pieces of cargo and therefore an additional correction based on the beam and the GM of the vessel must be applied to the transverse acceleration figure. This correction factor can be obtained from Table 4.

If the vessel's Cargo Securing Manual contains tables for these acceleration then those tables should be used rather than the tables in Annex 13 to obtain the corrected acceleration.

The longitudinal and transverse forces produced by wind pressure and sea sloshing can be calculated from the dimensions of the unit on the basis that each force is assumed to be 1 kN per m^2 of the exposed forward or side face of the unit, except that sea sloshing forces need only be applied to a height on the unit of no more than 2 m above the weather deck or hatch top where the piece is in stowage.

STEP TWO - EXTERNAL FORCES

F_x, F_y and F_z can now be calculated, using the basic formula.

When assessing the transverse tipping of the cargo the balance calculation is based upon the transverse force (F_y) multiplied by the lever-arm of tipping (a). For simplicity, this external force of tipping (named F_yt here) should be calculated at the same time as the other external forces, where: $F_yt = F_y.a$.

Then we have the four external forces we need. We need F_z for the calculation of the anti-longitudinal sliding force and F_x, F_y and F_yt for the final balance assessment.

STEP THREE - FRICTION AND LASHINGS

We now move on to the calculation for the strength and effectiveness of the lashings.

When the number, type and location of the securing arrangements have been decided upon their holding-down power, so to speak, and the associated frictional forces can then be calculated in terms of forces acting against transverse sliding, transverse tipping and longitudinal sliding.

First, the MSL of each component is found and then the MSL of the weakest link in each lashing is listed. MSLs should be listed in kilo-Newtons (kN) for use in the calculations where 1 kN is taken to equal 100 kg (or 10 kN = 1 tonne).

The strength of each lashing used in these calculations is called the "calculated strength" (CS). The calculated strength of the lashings will be the MSL of the weakest part of the lashing arrangement, as described above, divided by a safety factor of 1.5. This safety factor allows for the possibility of an uneven distribution of the forces among the lashing devices and any reduced strength because of the improper assembly of the devices, or any other unknown factors.

For the calculation of the anti-sliding forces the "f-Value", which is a function of the angle of the lashing to the horizontal (a) and the friction between the unit and the deck (μ), must be applied to the calculated strength of each device; f-Values are obtained from Table 5. The f-Value for each lashing can be listed on the calculation sheet.

With regard to the longitudinal anti-sliding force calculation, it must be remembered that the longitudinal component of the transverse securing devices should not be assumed to be greater than 0.5 of the calculated strength of each of those lashings. Bearing this in mind, when calculating the effectiveness of each lashing, only those lashings which have a fore-and-aft component should be used and that component should be reduced by at least 50%. For guidance, only lashings which are at an angle of more than 20° to the athwartships line should be used in the calculation. Also, only those which lead in the direction being considered, either forward or aft, should be used in the calculation for the anti-sliding force for that direction and those lashings which are at an angle to the athwartships line of 20° or less should be ignored in both longitudinal anti-sliding calculations.

With regard to the force acting against transverse tipping, the lever arm for each lashing, that is the perpendicular distance between the tipping point, or tipping axis of the cargo unit and each lashing (c), must be applied to the calculated strength of each lashing. These c-values can be listed for each lashing on the calculation sheet.

With all the necessary parts listed, the corrected calculated strength for each lashing, applying the f-Value or the c-value where appropriate can be found by:-

CS.f = MSL. Safety Factor. f-Value

CS.c = MSL. Safety Factor. c-value

These can then be added together for each direction and type to give sums (Σ CS.f and ΣCS.c) for inclusion in Step Four.

STEP FOUR - ANTI-MOVEMENT FORCES AND BALANCE ASSESSMENT

The anti-transverse sliding force can be calculated by multiplying together the friction coefficient, the mass of the unit and the acceleration due to gravity (g) and then adding to that figure the appropriate sum of corrected calculation strengths (Σ CS.f). This calculation should be done for each direction, port and starboard.

The total anti-tipping force can be calculated using the mass of the unit multiplied by gravity (g) and the lever arm of stableness (b), which is the horizontal distance between the tipping point and the centre of gravity of the unit, and then by adding on the appropriate sum of corrected calculated strengths (Σ CS.c). This transverse tipping calculation should be done for each side, port as well as starboard.

The anti-longitudinal sliding force can be calculated using the mass of the unit (m), gravity (g), the external vertical force (F_z) the coefficient of friction (μ) and the appropriate sum of corrected strengths (Σ CS.f). This calculation should be done for each direction, forward and aft.

The three formulae to be used from Annex 13, are as follows:-

Transverse anti-sliding force = $\mu.m.g + CS_1.f_1 + CS_2.f_2 + ... + CS_n.f_n$

Transverse anti-tipping force = $b.m.g + CS_1.c_1 + CS_2.c_2 + ... + CS_n.c_n$

Longitudinal anti-sliding force = $\mu.(m.g - F_z) + CS_1.f_1 + CS_2.f_2 + ... + CS_n.f_n$

When the anti-sliding and anti-tipping forces have been calculated the final balance assessment can be done; those forces can be equated to the appropriate external forces. If the anti-sliding/anti-tipping forces are greater than the opposing external forces then the proposed lashing arrangements may be considered sufficient for the voyage. The three equations to be used are as follows:-

$F_y \leq$ Transverse anti-sliding force

$F_y.a \leq$ Transverse anti-tipping force

$F_x \leq$ Longitudinal anti-sliding force

To summarise, therefore, the Advanced Calculation Method is a series of calculations to determine whether or not longitudinal, transverse and vertical external forces are more than balanced by the anti-sliding and anti-tipping components of the combination of the proposed lashing system and the friction between the base of the unit and the deck upon which it is stowed.

Attached as **Appendix E** is a blank form which may be completed to calculate the various parts to determine the balance of forces and movements.

APPENDIX D - ADVANCED CALCULATION METHOD - WORKED EXAMPLE

There is, in Annex 13 of the CSS Code, a simplified example of how the Advanced Calculation Method is used. Below is given a more practical demonstration of how the method is used in conjunction with the calculation sheet developed for this guide.

The motor vessel "NEPANDI" is scheduled to carry a large boiler of weight 81.7 tonnes, on-deck, from Liverpool to Mumbai. The boiler has been prepared for carriage on-deck, that is to say there are no openings which might allow entry of water and wetting by sea or rain will not cause damage; the shippers have confirmed this in writing. The weather deck hatch covers have sufficient strength, being strengthened for containers, so long as the weight is spread by sufficient timber. Departure from Liverpool will be on 17th September and the e.t.a. has been given by the master as 10th October, allowing three days for the Suez Canal transit.

The voyage will be south to Gibraltar, east in the Mediterranean Sea to Port Said, through the Suez Canal into the Red Sea and finally across the Gulf of Arabia to Mumbai. The weather in the North Atlantic to Gibraltar is likely to be moderate with a 5% possibility of winds of Beaufort force 7 or higher and with associated heavy swell conditions. In the Mediterranean Sea conditions should be good. The south-west monsoon begins in the Arabian Sea during June and ends, in the waters off Mumbai at the end of September. Bearing the above in mind the worst weather likely to be experienced by "NEPANDI" will be during the first week of the voyage. Detailed weather forecasts should therefore be obtained, and if adverse weather is forecast, that is winds of more than force 5, the departure from Liverpool can be delayed until severe adverse weather has passed, or additional lashings can be fitted.

The basic details of the vessel, the item of cargo and the lashings, which are needed for the calculation are as follows:-

The vessel - NEPANDI

Length	157 m
Beam	22 m
GM	1.8 m
Speed	14.0 kts

Stowage at 120 m from aft = 0.76 L
Stowage on timber - Coefficient $\mu = 0.3$

The cargo - Boiler

Weight	81.7 tonnes
Length	6.3 m
Height	6.0 m
Width	3.4 m at base
C of G	2.1 m above base
	1.7 m in from sides

Lashing points rated at 20 tonnes each
Therefore MSL at 50% = 10 tonnes

The lashings

Wire	-	18mm diameter galvanised 6 x 24 – 13.2 tonnes breaking strength MSL at 80% = 10.56 tonnes MSL at 70% = 9.24 tonnes (bulldog grip eyes)		
Shackles	-	large D type – marked SWL 20 tonnes MSL at 50% = 10.0 tonnes		
Turnbuckles	-	Hamburger type -	Rod length	500 m
		-	Rod diameter	30 mm
		-	Bow diameter	18 mm
		-	Breaking strength	19.0 tonnes
		MSL at 50% = 9.5 tonnes		
D - rings	-	container fittings rated at 35 tonnes. MSL at 50% = 17.5 tonnes		

The governing component is the wire at MSL = 9.24 tonnes or 92.4 kN.

The following sketch shows the layout of the lashings fitted to the boiler, and gives the lashing angles and lever arms.

The calculation using all the above information shows that the boiler is satisfactorily lashed in all four directions because the six anti-movement forces acting against sliding and tipping, are all greater than the external forces by an acceptable margin, see below.

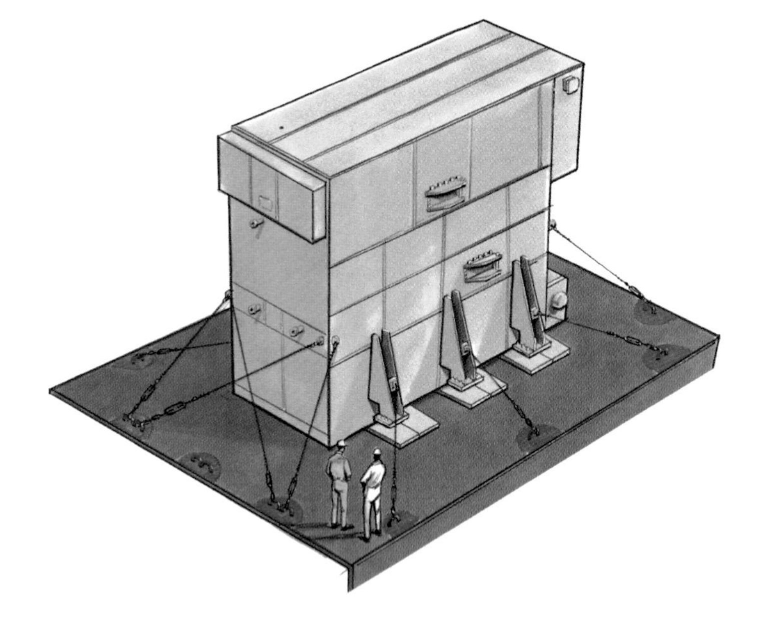

81.7 tonne boiler stowed on deck - layout of lashings (for illustration purposes only).

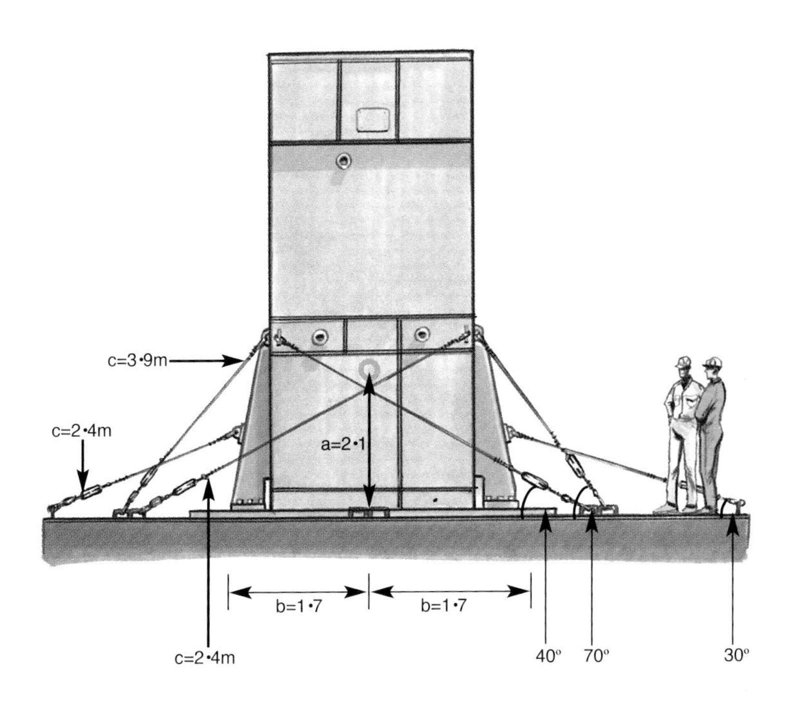
c=3·9m
c=2·4m
a=2·1
b=1·7
b=1·7
c=2·4m
40°
70°
30°

ADVANCED METHOD OF CALCULATION FORM

Vessel: NEPANDI — **Voyage No. 1**
Load Port: LIVERPOOL — **Discharge Port: MUMBAI**
Load Date: 17th September — **Discharge Date: 11th October**
Cargo Type: BOILER

STEP ONE - Inputs and Primary Calculations

SHIP		CARGO	
Length	157	Width	3.4
Breadth	22	Length	6.3
GM	1.8	Height	6
Speed	14	Mass (m)	81.7
B/GM	12.2	Longitudinal position	0.76
Table 3 correction T3	0.7	Vertical position	3
Table 4 correction T4	1.04	Friction (μ)	0.3
Longitudinal acceleration - Table 2 a_x	2.9	Lever arm of tipping (a)	2.1
Transverse acceleration - Table 2 a_y	6.4	Lever arm of stableness (b) port	1.7
Vertical acceleration - Table 2 a_z	7.04	Lever arm of stableness (b) starboard	1.7
		Wind pressure longitudinal (Fw_x)	20.4
Longitudinal acceleration corrected a_x	2.03	Wind pressure transverse (Fw_y)	37.8
Transverse acceleration corrected a_y	4.66	Sea slosh longitudinal (Fs_x)	6.8
Vertical acceleration corrected a_z	4.93	Sea slosh transverse (Fs_y)	12.6

STEP TWO - External forces

Longitudinal sliding	$F_x = m.a_x + Fw_x + Fs_x$	81.7	x	2.03	+	20.4	+	6.8	=	193.1
Transverse sliding	$F_y = m.a_y + Fw_x + Fs_y$	81.7	x	4.66	+	37.8	+	12.6	=	431.1
Transverse tipping	$F_{yt} = F_y.a$					431.1	x	2.1	=	905.4
Vertical	$F_z = m.a_z$					81.7	x	4.93	=	402.8

STEP THREE - Friction and Lashings

Port Side	*1*	*2*	*3*	*4*	*5*	*6*	*7*	*8*	*9*	*10*		
MSL	92.4	92.4	92.4	92.4	92.4	92.4						
Lashing angle (α)	40	70	30	30	30	40						
f - value - Table 5	0.96	0.62	1.02	1.02	1.02	0.96						
Lever arm of securing (c)	2.4	3.9	2.4	2.4	2.4	2.4						
Safety factor	***0.67***	***0.67***	***0.67***	***0.67***	***0.67***	***0.67***	***0.67***	***0.67***	***0.67***	***0.67***		
CS.f (MSL . Safety factor . f)	5.94	3.84	6.31	6.31	6.31	5.94					**Σ(sum)**	346.5
CS.c (MSL . Safety factor . c)	148.6	241.4	148.6	148.6	148.6	148.6					**Σ(sum)**	984.4

Starboard Side	1	2	3	4	5	6	7	8	9	10		
MSL	92.4	92.4	92.4	92.4	92.4	92.4						
Lashing angle (α)	40	70	30	30	30	40						
f - value - Table 5	0.96	0.62	1.02	1.02	1.02	0.96						
Lever arm of securing (c)	2.4	3.9	2.4	2.4	2.4	2.4						
Safety factor	***0.67***	***0.67***	***0.67***	***0.67***	***0.67***	***0.67***	***0.67***	***0.67***	***0.67***	***0.67***		
CS.f (MSL . Safety factor . f)	5.94	3.84	6.31	6.31	6.31	5.94					**Σ(sum)**	346.5
CS.c(MSL . Safety factor . c)	148.6	241.4	148.6	148.6	148.6	148.6					**Σ(sum)**	984.4
Longitudinal Forward	***1***	***2***	***3***	***4***	***5***	***6***	***7***	***8***	***9***	***10***		
MSL	92.4	92.4	92.4	92.4	92.4	92.4						
Lashing angle (α)	30	70	40	40	70	30						
f - value - Table 5	1.02	0.62	0.96	0.96	0.62	1.02						
Safety factor	***0.67***	***0.67***	***0.67***	***0.67***	***0.67***	***0.67***	***0.67***	***0.67***	***0.67***	***0.67***		
Longitudinal Component Proportion	0.5	0.5	0.5	0.5	0.5	0.5						
CS.f (MSL . Safety factor . f) Corr'd	31.57	19.25	29.7	29.7	19.25	31.57					**Σ(sum)**	161.05
Longitudinal Aft	***1***	***2***	***3***	***4***	***5***	***6***	***7***	***8***	***9***	***10***		
MSL	92.4	92.4	92.4	92.4								
Lashing angle (α)	30	40	40	30								
f - value - Table 5	1.02	0.96	0.96	1.02								
Safety factor	***0.67***	***0.67***	***0.67***	***0.67***	***0.67***	***0.67***	***0.67***	***0.67***	***0.67***	***0.67***		
Longitudinal Component Proportion	0.5	0.5	0.5	0.5								
CS.f (MSL . Safety factor . f) Corr'd	31.57	29.7	29.7	31.57							**Σ(sum)**	122.55

STEP FOUR - Anti-movement forces and Balance Assessment

											E forces	Yes/No
Transverse sliding port	μ.m.g + ΣCS.f	0.3	x	81.7	x	*9.81*	+	346.5	=	586.9	431.1	Y
Transverse sliding starboard	μ.m.g + ΣCS.f	0.3	x	81.7	x	*9.81*	+	346.5	=	586.9	431.1	Y
Transverse tipping port	b.m.g + ΣCS.c	1.7	x	81.7	x	*9.81*	+	984.4	=	2346.9	905.4	Y
Transverse tipping starboard	b.m.g + ΣCS.c	1.7	x	81.7	x	*9.81*	+	984.4	=	2346.9	905.4	Y
Longitudinal sliding forward	μ(m.g-F_z)ΣCS.f	0.3	(81.7	x	*9.81*	-	412.6)	+161.05	=	277.7	193.1	Y
Longitudinal sliding aft	μ(m.g-F_z)ΣCS.f	0.3	(81.7	x	*9.81*	-	412.6)	+122.55	=	239.2	193.1	Y

APPENDIX E - ADVANCED CALCULATION METHOD - BLANK FORM

ADVANCED METHOD OF CALCULATION FORM

Vessel:	**Voyage No.**
Load Port:	**Discharge Port:**
Load Date	**Discharge Date:**
Cargo Type:	

STEP ONE - Inputs and Primary Calculations

SHIP		**CARGO**		
Length		Width		
Breadth		Length		
GM		Height		
Speed		Mass (m)		
B/GM		Longitudinal position		
Table 3 correction T3		Vertical position		
Table 4 correction T4		Friction (μ)		
Longitudinal acceleration - Table 2 a_x		Lever arm of tipping (a)		
Transverse acceleration - Table 2 a_y		Lever arm of stableness (b) port		
Vertical acceleration - Table 2 a_z		Lever arm of stableness (b) starboard		
		Wind pressure longitudinal (Fw_x)		
Longitudinal acceleration corrected a_x		Wind pressure transverse (Fw_y)		
Transverse acceleration corrected a_y		Sea slosh longitudinal (Fs_x)		
Vertical acceleration corrected a_z		Sea slosh transverse (Fs_y)		

STEP TWO - External forces

Longitudinal sliding	$F_x = m.a_x + Fw_x + Fs_x$		x		+		+		=	
Transverse sliding	$F_y = m.a_y + Fw_x + Fs_y$		x		+		+		=	
Transverse tipping	$F_{yt} = F_y.a$						x		=	
Vertical	$F_z = m.a_z$						x		=	

STEP THREE - Friction and Lashings

Port Side	*1*	*2*	*3*	*4*	*5*	*6*	*7*	*8*	*9*	*10*		
MSL												
Lashing angle (α)												
f - value - Table 5												
Lever arm of securing (c)												
Safety factor	*0.67*	*0.67*	*0.67*	*0.67*	*0.67*	*0.67*	*0.67*	*0.67*	*0.67*	*0.67*		
CS.f (MSL . Safety factor . f)											**Σ(sum)**	
CS.c(MSL . Safety factor . c)											**Σ(sum)**	

Starboard Side	1	2	3	4	5	6	7	8	9	10		
MSL												
Lashing angle (α)												
f - value - Table 5												
Lever arm of securing (c)												
Safety factor	0.67	0.67	0.67	0.67	0.67	0.67	0.67	0.67	0.67	0.67		
CS.f (MSL . Safety factor . f)											Σ(sum)	
CS.c(MSL . Safety factor . c)											Σ(sum)	
Longitudinal Forward	1	2	3	4	5	6	7	8	9	10		
MSL												
Lashing angle (α)												
f - value - Table 5												
Safety factor	0.67	0.67	0.67	0.67	0.67	0.67	0.67	0.67	0.67	0.67		
Longitudinal Component Proportion												
CS.f (MSL . Safety factor . f) Corr'd											Σ(sum)	
Longitudinal Aft	1	2	3	4	5	6	7	8	9	10		
MSL												
Lashing angle (α)												
f - value - Table 5												
Safety factor	0.67	0.67	0.67	0.67	0.67	0.67	0.67	0.67	0.67	0.67		
Longitudinal Component Proportion												
CS.f (MSL . Safety factor . f) Corr'd											Σ(sum)	

STEP FOUR - Anti-movement forces and Balance Assessment

											E forces	Yes/No
Transverse sliding port	μ.m.g + ΣCS.f		x		x	9.81	+		=			
Transverse sliding starboard	μ.m.g + ΣCS.f		x		x	9.81	+		=			
Transverse tipping port	b.m.g + ΣCS.c		x		x	9.81	+		=			
Transverse tipping starboard	b.m.g + ΣCS.c		x		x	9.81	+		=			
Longitudinal sliding forward	$\mu(m.g-F_z)$ΣCS.f		(	x	9.81	-	)	+	=			
Longitudinal sliding aft	$\mu(m.g-F_z)$ΣCS.f		(	x	9.81	-	)	+	=			

BIBLIOGRAPHY

IMO: Code on Intact Stability for All Types of Ships Covered by IMO Instruments, (International Maritime Organization, 1995) IMO-874E ISBN 92 801 1334 8

IMO: Code of Safe Practice for Cargo Stowage and Securing (CSS Code), (Consolidated Edition, International Maritime Organization, 2003) IMO-IA292E

IMO: Code of Safe Practice for Ships Carrying Timber Deck Cargoes, (International Maritime Organization, 1991) IMO-275E ISBN 92 801 1285 6

IMO/ILO/UN ECE: Guidelines for Packing Cargo in Cargo Transport Units, (International Maritime Organization, 1997) IMO-284E ISBN 92 801 1318 6

IMO: Guidelines for the Preparation of the Cargo Securing Manual, (International Maritime Organization, 1997) IMO-298E ISBN 92 801 1441 7

Maritime and Coastguard Agency: The Carriage of Cargoes, Volume 1 - The carriage of packaged cargoes and cargo units (including containers and vehicles), Instructions for the Guidance of Surveyors, (The Stationery Office, 1993) ISBN 0 11 552113 5

Knott: Lashing and Securing of Deck Cargoes, (3rd edn, The Nautical Institute, 2002) ISBN 18700 7718 0

Sparks: Steel - Carriage by Sea, (3rd edn, LLP Limited, 1999) ISBN 1 85978 891 2

Rankin: Thomas' Stowage, (4th edn, Brown, Son & Ferguson Ltd, 2002) ISBN 0 85174 694 2

INDEX